Professional
Systems Development

Business Information Technology Series

Series Editor: TONY GUNTON

Professional Systems Development

Experience, ideas and action

Niels Erik Andersen
Finn Kensing
Jette Lundin
Lars Mathiassen
Andreas Munk-Madsen
Monika Rasbech
Pål Sørgaard

Prentice Hall
New York London Toronto Sydney Tokyo

First published 1990 by
Prentice Hall International (UK) Ltd,
66 Wood Lane End, Hemel Hempstead,
Hertfordshire, HP2 4RG
A division of
Simon & Schuster International Group

© 1990 Prentice Hall International (UK) Ltd

The original edition of this work was published in Denmark by Teknisk Forlag,
Copenhagen, under the title *Professionel Systemudvikling: Erfaringer, muligheder og handling*
© 1986 Teknisk Forlag A/S.

Printed and bound in Great Britain at
the University Press, Cambridge

Library of Congress Cataloging-in-Publication Data

Professional systemudvikling. English.
    Professional systems development: experience, ideas, and action/
Niels Erik Andersen ... [et al.].
        p.   cm. — (Business information technology series)
    Includes bibliographical references.
    ISBN 0-13-725540-3
    1. System design.   I. Andersen, Niels Erik. II. Title.
III. Series.
    QA76.9.S88P76313   1990
    004.2'1—dc20   89-23202
                                                                CIP

British Library Cataloguing in Publication Data

Professional systems development: experience, ideas and
    action.
    1. Systems analysis
    I. Andersen, Niels Erik   II. Series   III. Professional
    Systemudvikling. *English*
    003

    ISBN 0-13-725540-3 hbk.
    ISBN 0-13-725524-1 pbk.

---

            1   2   3   4   5   94   93   92   91   90
        ISBN 0-13-725540-3

To Kristen Nygaard
for all the years
of provocation —
and support.

Overview

Contents

Part III   Changing Working Practices in Systems Development

Preface

Computer technology is often presented as a unique symbol of future and progress. There are, of course, certain realities behind this. Some of the most radical changes in society during the last 40 years have been related to development and use of computer based systems. Working within the field, we know, however, that there often is a considerable gap between symbols and realities. The daily life of a system developer is marked as much with problems, failures and conflicts as with success and progress.

This book attempts to bridge the gap between ideals and reality within systems development. We have tried to start out from today's reality. We think that one of the most important assets of a systems development project is the experience of the participants. Our recommendations in this book are based on this principle. Moreover, systems development is a creative activity in which it is important to look at possibilities and options. One of the goals of the book is therefore to enrich the systems developers' understanding of what they can do. Finally, we have tried to orient the book towards action. The book is intended to inspire and provoke the reader to change working practices — changes that could be a step away from today's realities towards a more ideal situation.

We want systems development to grow as a discipline in its own right. We want to promote a professional attitude. We want to be proud of the possibilities related to our field, and at the same time humble with respect to its limitations. The subject of the book is systems development, but the book does not intend to cover all relevant subjects. We have tried to relate theory and practice, and the book should be seen as a supplement to books presenting specific methods and techniques.

The book is written for practitioners, and as indicated in the last chapter of the book, it is intended as a handbook to support and improve practical work. The book can be used by individual persons, in smaller study groups, or in more traditional course activities. At the same time, the book has, however, proved successful as course material for students of systems development. When the students have learned about one or two conventional systems development methods, the book gives them an overview and a conceptual background for comparing methods and evaluating practical cases and experiences.

The book was originally published in Danish in 1986, based on an intensive empirical research effort, the MARS project. MARS is a Danish acronym for 'Systematic Working Practices in Systems Development'. In the MARS project we investigated how systems development is carried out in practice, and we experimented with different ways of changing working practices. The project was designed as an action oriented research effort, and lots of practical experience and empirical evidence were compiled. Through the project we learned about the reality of systems development and we came to appreciate the difficulties and challenges related to changing working practices. In this book we have tried to present these insights in a useful and coherent way. In addition, the MARS project has been reported in a number of more traditional reports and articles. The project was carried out by researchers and students from the Computer Science Departments at the Universities of Aarhus and Roskilde in cooperation with systems developers from four organizations: EAC Data, Jutland Telephone, RC 79, and the Computing Centre of the Danish Savings Banks. The MARS project was supported financially by The Danish Council of Technology, The Danish Natural Science Research Council, and Dansk Datamatik Center.

We wish to thank all those who have contributed to the MARS project and to this book. Practitioners have been prepared to tell about their problems and relate to our thinking. Researchers and students have taken their time to discuss and criticize. Secretaries, technical staff and editors have made it possible for us to present our ideas and results to a larger audience.

Niels Erik Andersen
Finn Kensing
Jette Lundin
Lars Mathiassen
Andreas Munk-Madsen
Monika Rasbech
Pål Sørgaard

Aarhus, 1989

1 Systems development — many possibilities

See it as a challenge

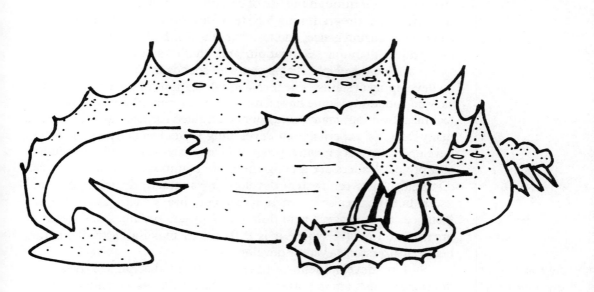

1.1 Systems development
— a challenge

Systems development consists of those activities which aim at changing an organization through the use of computer technology. This includes activities like programming, system description, feasibility study, conversion, maintenance, and training of users. It also includes activities like project planning, estimation, and quality assurance.

A system developer is a person who spends most of his or her time on developing systems. The formal qualifications of system developers vary considerably: some have a university degree; others have received technical training; many have not been trained formally at all, but have many years of experience in developing system. The titles of system developers also vary greatly: programmers, system analysts, consultants, and project leaders are among the more common. Normally one can distinguish between system developers, salesmen, dp managers, and users, but the precise distinctions are not always clear. There are, for instance, dp managers who do a lot of programming. New forms of organization evolve where it is difficult to make a clear distinction between users and system developers.

Systems development requires knowledge from many professions

System development is based on many disciplines. A system developer must, among other things, master the mathematical aspects of programming, the sociological aspects of organizational development, and the psychological aspects of designing man—machine interfaces. A system developer must be a good designer who can put new things together, a good analyst who can understand the working situation of others, and a good politician who can handle a project characterized by uncertainty and conflict. Systems development requires knowledge from many professions. In practice, however, it is impossible for one system developer to master them all. That is why it is necessary to establish cooperation between people with different educational backgrounds and with different experiences. The professional system developer can create a process where different qualifications are exploited.

> **Exercise 1.1**
>
> **Evaluation of current qualifications**
>
> What are you good at? What would you like to be better at?
> What is your project, your department, or the company
> in which you are employed good at? Where should it improve?

1.2 Typical problems

In practice there will always be problems: because of time pressure, because it is impossible to predict the course of the project, or because it is difficult to handle the challenges. These problems should not be swept under the carpet; they should be brought out in the open so that one can learn from one's mistakes and the mistakes of others.

The principal message of this book is that system developers must reflect systematically on their own practice. To illustrate this point the stories of six projects observed by the authors are told briefly.

Insufficient analysis

During the development of a production control system, the system developers became frustrated because the users did not comment on their design proposals. The project was at a standstill waiting for user approval. In order to get better response the system developers decided to develop a prototype. Two man-years were spent on developing the prototype, but the users still did not have any comments. Only then did the system developers study the users' work situation. They found that the system would be of no help to the users in their work. The idea to develop the system had originated from another organizational unit which hoped to gain more control over the way the prospective users organized their work.

The problem was that the system developers had failed to analyse the user organization sufficiently. They spent their time programming instead of reflecting on the situation.

Unreflected design process

Apply different working practices

A project developing an order-handling system included an activity called general design. The system had been divided into three parts which were treated in the same way. However, the problems connected to the three subsystems were not the same:

- One subsystem had a very well-defined function (inventory simulation), but it was not clear how it should model reality. An analysis of the users' work was needed.

- The function of the second subsystem was unclear, but was based on a well-defined model of reality. Experimental design was needed.

- The third subsystem was based on a well-defined model of reality, and a number of functions on different levels of ambition had been defined. All that remained to be done was to decide which level of ambition to choose.

The system developers had many meetings discussing the system with the users. It took them more than a year to find the right course of action. The problem was that the system developers did not realize that there was a need for analysis, design, and decision making, respectively, where the three subsystems were concerned, and that the working practices had to be adapted according to the different tasks. What they should have done was to evaluate the situation in each of the three cases, and base their working practices on these evaluations.

No baselines

Division of labour requires a shared and explicit understanding of the project

Four people in a project were working on overall technical design. The project was behind schedule and would not be able to meet the deadline stipulated in the contract, so management decided to increase the staff assigned to the project. During the next nine months an average of 18 people worked in the project. The new people were supposed to produce detailed design and code. The overall design was not finished when the project group was enlarged, so the new people were divided into four groups, each of which was headed by one of the original four designers. Coordination among the groups was oral and informal.

The overall design was never completed. The situation was more or less chaotic during those nine months, and it was difficult to see whether the project made any real progress. Only when the client postponed the deadline and the staff was reduced to nine people did things begin to move forward. Now it was possible to base the detailed design and the coding on a mutual informal understanding of the product — an understanding which the project members after all had gained during the nine months of chaos.

The problem here was that the project had additional people assigned to it at a time when the project was not standing on a baseline. A baseline is a well-defined project state which allows local planning and progress in the project's subgroups. Before more people are assigned to a project it is important to evaluate the state of the project in order to ensure that the provision of resources will produce the intended results.

As the project was not at a baseline, nobody knew the exact situation. Management did not reflect on this fact, it made a panic decision, it acted blindly.

Incomplete test

In a project developing an accounting system a central component of the system was not installed until ten days before the planned delivery date. Consequently the system developers did not have time to perform a proper test. The system was put into production in spite of this because the system was important to the user organization. As could be expected the system proved to have many program errors. Only the system developers could see whether a system defect was caused by an error made by the users, an application-program error, or a software error. Consequently the system developers had to operate the system themselves during the next nine months.

The problem was that the inadequate test resulted in a permanent firefighting situation which lasted for nine months during which no new development was possible. A lot of energy went into this firefighting. Very little energy was spent on reflecting on the situation.

Many postponements

*Planning
requires
estimation*

In a project developing a new terminal system the schedule was worked
out by counting backwards from the required date of delivery. The state
and conditions of the project were not analysed or acknowledged. This
resulted in many changes in the plans. For instance the overall functional
design at one point was promised to be finished in three months. After
several postponements the design was delivered twenty-one months after
the original deadline. The development organization's prestige suffered
a hard blow.

The system developers concentrated on conforming the project to the illusions of a bureaucratic organization. A more professional attitude is recommended, with emphasis on estimates founded in project realities.

Narrow communication lines

Five months before the planned date of delivery the system developers in another project acknowledged that they would be delayed due to an increased level of ambition. More than three months were to pass, however, before it was decided what could be done about this problem. Later the system developers explained that it had been difficult to arrange a steering committee meeting so that a decision could be made. And besides, they expected that the user organization would have to ask for a postponement as it was delayed in its preliminary work.

A steering committee meeting must be planned well ahead of time. It is a poor excuse that it is hard to get the steering committee to meet. One risks losing credibility by waiting for others to ask for a postponement rather than being honest about one's own problems. What this project needed was more transparency based on the reflections of the system developers.

Need for professional working practices

These examples illustrate typical problems in systems development projects. The examples demonstrate that systems development is a complex process. Unpredictable situations arise, and the system developers must be able to interpret problematic situations and act accordingly. Professional systems development requires competent and active reflection before, during, and after the project.

1.3 Are you a professional?

Some system developers think that their most important task is to avoid failure. They are busy thinking up excuses of why their current work cannot be done any better. It is not this defeatist attitude that this book wishes to promote.

Nor is the idea to make it easier for bluffers. Like everyone else they make lots of mistakes — but they spend a lot of time covering them up. Sometimes it looks as though they have obtained some good

Amateur.

Bluffer.

Professional.

results. Time, however, will prove differently. Bluffers will probably not waste their time reading this book — they already know it all.

The idea of this book is to promote a professional attitude to systems development. What really counts is high quality of work, of products, and of services. The professional system developer sees a challenge in difficult tasks. Easy tasks offer the opportunity to experiment with or perfect one's working practices. Professional system developers do not work in projects without making errors, encountering problems, or facing conflicts. Only bluffers try to make their projects look flawless. Professional system developers analyse the mistakes of others as well as their own — and learn from them. They identify the important problems and try to solve them. They are aware of conflicts and try to let them surface in the right environment.

Design working practices on the basis of the situation

Professional system developers know what types of activities they are to work with, and they also know under which conditions they have to work. On the basis of this knowledge they organize their working practices by selecting from the repertoire of techniques and tools they have at their disposal. The professional system developer also tries to expand this repertoire by studying literature, with suggestions for improving working practices. Not all suggestions are equally applicable or accessible — but this is no excuse, it is a challenge.

How can the soil be prepared for professional systems development? It cannot be done in one day, and it is not easy. Professionalism flourishes in an environment where working practices are continually discussed and changed. It cannot be done once and for all — development within the field of computers is too rapid and the tasks too different. There is no standard method which helps to solve all problems. It is, however, possible to select a method, and from this method to design and change the working practices in the individual projects. To change working practices requires that the system developers are actively involved, and it requires energy and imagination. It will not do to leave the responsibility for this work solely to the individual system developer. He or she may not have the required extra energy.

An environment and a tradition for professional systems development should therefore contain elements such as the following:

- Active system developers.
- Sufficient resources.
- Exchange and evaluation of experience.
- Study of literature.

Exercise 1.2

Why professional?

Draw up a list of what you see as the major differences between a really good athlete and an amateur.

How would you characterize a competent (a professional) system developer?

Exercise 1.3

Need for change?

What did you do in your last project?

Did you observe a need for changing the working practices? If yes, what changes are needed?

1.4 About this book

This book has been written as an aid to system developers. Changing working practices is the main theme. Sometimes system developers need practical directions, so the book contains references and descriptions of selected methods. Sometimes they need to understand systems development better. Theory can be a help to understand fuzzy project situations better: theoretical understanding makes it possible to put thoughts into words. Theory can be a help both in selecting a method and in evaluating and exchanging experience. The book also contains a number of practical examples. These have been instructive to the authors of this book, and it is hoped that these examples will make it easier for the reader to relate to the subject matter.

The book falls into three parts. The first part (Chapters 2 and 3) presents and clarifies the concepts and ideas applied throughout the book. It contains the authors' research conclusions in the form of fundamental principles for systems development. Part of this material may be a little heavy and will require a second reading before it falls into place. The reader who needs more practical directions may skip the first part, and return to the more theoretical chapters later.

The second part of the book (Chapters 4 to 10) contains advice and suggestions for various aspects of project work. The reader will get some answers, but look in vain for others. Some techniques are described only briefly, but each chapter is followed by a list of further reading.

- Chapter 4 discusses how projects should be established. This is the first activity of a project, and it is the best opportunity to create good cooperation in the project.

- Chapter 5 discusses planning. System developers often have the advantage of being allowed to plan their own work. That is why they have to be good planners. The chapter includes some useful checklists to be applied when planning the project.

- Chapter 6 discusses project evaluation. A prerequisite of successful intervention into a critical project situation is an understanding of the situation. The chapter will present various evaluation techniques, including reviews which are suitable for following up on the quality of intermediate products, and which form a good basis for the future work in the project.

- Chapter 7 discusses baselines. A baseline is a well-defined project state which allows local planning and continued progress in the project's subgroups. It is a good idea to think in terms of baselines when planning or evaluating a project.

- Chapter 8 discusses cooperation with the users in analysis and design. System developers need users to be able to make good systems. The chapter includes an outline of some of the techniques that support the cooperation between users and system developers when analysing and designing systems.

- Chapter 9 discusses descriptions and description processes in analysis and design. What kind of descriptions are made, and what are they used for? What is the relationship between description and reality, and what kinds of abstractions are used in descriptions? These questions are answered in this chapter, and the chapter also presents an outline of various working practices and perspectives to be considered when organizing the description activities.

- Chapter 10 discusses firefighting — the situation where the system developers struggle to keep a poorly working system going. What do you do when you find yourself in firefighting situations all the time, and it looks as though it never will stop?

The third part of the book (Chapters 11 to 13) discusses how to change working practices, i.e. what you do when you have an idea of how it could be done, but not how you turn this idea into reality. Some changes require an effort at company level. Chapter 11 discusses various strategies for changing working practices. The chapter contains a concrete suggestion for how the work can be organized. Some changes can be effected directly in the projects, even if a corresponding effort is not made at company level. Chapter 12 describes what can be done in the individual projects. Chapter 13 contains directions and suggestions for how to use this book in projects, in study groups, or in changing working practices in general in the development organization.

Further reading

The examples of problems in practical systems development in Section 1.2 are described and analysed in more detail in MARS 2 (1984), MARS 3 (1984), MARS 4 (1984), and MARS 5 (1984).

Part I
Theory on Systems Development

2 Situation and action

Death to standard methods

Many system developers have the idealistic notion that projects can go according to standards and given guidelines. Section 2.1 illustrates why this is not always the case in real life projects. In some cases the system developers can rely on routine, but in other cases they need to experiment or make a mental effort to be able to understand and handle the situation. Section 2.2 describes three types of situations, each of which is characterized by different degrees of uncertainty, and discusses what is required to act and intervene in a project. Section 2.3 illustrates why system developers must actively establish and regulate a project and its relation to the surrounding environment: which aspects in the environment are important? What makes a project an organizational unit?

The relationship between the system developers on the one hand and the users and user organization on the other hand is important. Section 2.4 discusses the practical possibilities for establishing cooperation between the project and the users. In some cases users and their unions may demand active involvement, but this may vary considerably.

Section 2.5 argues that professional system developers must have the possibility, and the willingness to increase and change their repertoire of working practices. Only in this way is it possible to act sensibly in different types of situations. At the same time system developers have to develop their skills in accordance with technical and organizational changes.

2.1 Ideal and reality

To believe in rationality is both naive and irrational

Many of the methods employed in systems development are based on a simple rational ideal (see Figure 2.1). They assume that the involved parties in a given project share the same clearly defined objectives, that resources are available and plentiful, and that it is possible to identify the different design options and their consequences on the basis of analyses. Many prefer to see themselves as rational system developers. They also prefer to believe that they have a very clear notion of what it is they wish to obtain before they start the project. And they prefer to have good reasons for choosing a certain solution or procedure over another.

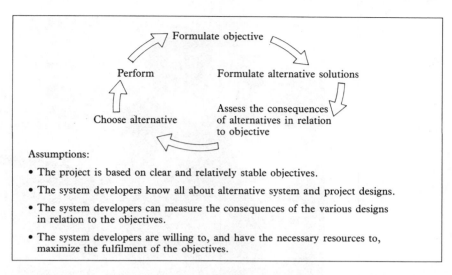

Figure 2.1   The rational ideal and the assumptions on which it is based.

However, projects usually take quite a different course. They start off without a clearly defined objective. Design decisions are taken before the alternatives have been investigated, and before the consequences have been analysed. What is the reason for this discrepancy? Is it because system developers have not yet become competent enough? Would they be able to make reality accord with the rational ideal if they worked in a more disciplined manner, and followed the common standards more strictly?

There are many reasons why system development projects cannot follow a rational ideal:

- In most cases the user organization does not know exactly what it wants, or the users are unable to describe what they know.

- Even if system developers knew the requirements, there are many other facts they must know before they can develop a system. Many important details only become clear later in the process, and design decisions may have to be revised.

- Experience has shown that even if system developers knew the relevant facts before they started, the complexity is often difficult to handle. During the project the system developers must separate the important from the unimportant. This requires experiments and mistakes cannot be avoided.

- Even if system developers could handle the relevant details, requirements still change in the course of almost all projects, and external relations even create conflicting requirements. Situations like that may require that new design decisions be made.

- Human error can only be avoided if we avoid human beings.

- The projects will usually be subjected to ideas from previous projects or from methods. Such ideas are not necessarily rationally linked to the requirements of the new system.

- Economy may force system developers to apply software or hardware which was intended for other purposes, or which is not yet finished and tested. The software and hardware is consequently considered adequate in light of the money saved, but does not necessarily meet the requirements of the project.

These are some of the reasons why system development projects cannot take a rational and unproblematic course. It would be professionally naive to think that system development projects can be made to follow a rational ideal. However, the above-mentioned fundamental characteristics of system development projects present an enormous professional challenge. If that challenge is not accepted, projects will inevitably slip off course because of random decisions or lack of intervention.

2.2 Situations and uncertainty

Take your starting point in the situations

During the course of a project different types of situations will arise, each of which makes special demands on the system developers. We distinguish between three types of situations which we call routine, problem solving, and problem setting situations, respectively (see Table 2.1). The three types of situations correspond to an increasing degree of uncertainty in the situation. It is easiest to predict the course of, and estimate the required effort in a routine situation; and it is hardest to do so in a problem setting situation.

Situation \ Attributes in relation to	Assignment or problem	Working practice	Uncertainty
Routine	Known	Known	Small
Problem solving	Known	Unknown	Intermediate
Problem setting	Unknown	Unknown	Large

Table 2.1   Characteristics of three different types of situation which arise in system development projects.

Routine

The problem and the task are known in routine situations, and so also are the correct working practices to apply to handle the task. The situation is routine when a module which can recognize input of a given format is to be programmed. The task is known, and it is known that a solution can be structured with the help of state-transition tables. The situation is also routine when it is announced at a project meeting that a sub-activity is finished ahead of schedule. The management task is known, and it is known that the situation requires adjustment of the original project plans.

The problem. A system development project takes its starting point in a more or less well-defined problem in the user organization.

Routine situations are easy to handle because they are known, and so is the method of handling them. However, routine situations may still require an extensive and qualified effort.

Problem solving

The task is known in problem-solving situations, but there is uncertainty or inadequate knowledge about which working practices to apply. A problem-solving situation arises when it is known that there are errors in a program. The task is clear, but it is not known exactly how to tackle the situation to find the error. A problem-solving situation also arises when one of the project group members is suddenly transferred to another project or leaves the company. The situation is clear, but it may be difficult to find an expedient way to intervene.

Problem-solving situations are open situations. They often require adoption of an experimental strategy. Problem-solving situations require mastery of different working practices to try to apply to the problem.

Problem setting

In problem-setting situations the whole situation is unclear to us. We know that we have to intervene in one way or another. But we do not know the problem or the task — and consequently we do not know what procedure to employ. If a project finds that the user organization rejects one design proposal after the other, the project group will know that something is wrong. But is it the design? Or is it because the user organization's original requirements do not reflect the current reality?

Another example is a project where the staffing of sub-tasks results in disagreements or bad feelings. This is also a problem-setting situation. Is the problem the way the assignments were allocated? Does the situation reflect personal conflicts in the group?

In problem-setting situations a number of symptoms become evident. From there the situation must be analysed to identify the problem or the task. There is no certainty, however, that it will be possible to define which problem or problems covers the situation. And if it is possible, there is no certainty that everyone involved will agree with the formulation of the problem. Various conflicting interpretations of the situation might emerge. There is a temptation to do nothing or try to cover up the situation, even though it is known or suspected that something is wrong.

System development projects contain, as described above, different types of situations, and this means that the system developer is facing two challenges.

System development projects require active and competent project cultivation

The first challenge is to be able to handle the various situations arising in a project. In problem-setting situations one may try to define the problem or the task, and in this way create a routine or problem-solving situation. In problem-solving situations one may make use of experiments to work out the appropriate working practices, thus creating a routine situation. System development projects cannot be formed merely on the basis of standards and given guidelines. They require active and competent project cultivation throughout the course of the project. System developers must be able to assess the situations in which they find themselves. They must be able to face problems and mistakes, and be open-minded with respect to the status of their own work and the project as a whole.

Another, more fundamental, challenge is to develop and change the repertoire of working practices. The degree of uncertainty in the project situation is determined by the experience and qualifications of the system developers participating in the project. For instance a situation might be a problem-setting situation to an inexperienced person, but a problem-solving (or even a routine) situation to a more experienced person. System developers must master a repertoire of working practices and must be willing and able to introduce new working practices in the project. They must not get stuck in traditions. New technical and organizational conditions make new demands, and system developers must therefore change and develop their repertoire of working practices.

Exercise 2.1

Discuss project situations

Choose a number of typical situations from your last project. Some of the situations should be concerned with actual project performance, others with project management.

Characterize each situation as either a routine, problem-solving, or problem-setting situation.

Discuss the working practices applied, and whether seeing the situations as either routine, problem-solving, or problem-setting situations helps you to consider more expedient working practices.

2.3 The project and its environment

It is necessary to know many aspects of the project and its environment to be able to understand and handle the different types of situations. Firstly the relations between the situations, the working practices and the conditions of the project are discussed. Secondly the mutual commitments, or contracts, between the project participants are examined. They are commitments on products and services, and they are important parts of the conditions of the project. Thirdly distinction is made between two different roles the project can play in relation to the user organization. Each of these roles describes general, ideal types of contractual arrangements. Sometimes one is free to choose whether one will play the role of a consultant or that of a supplier, sometimes the role is given as a condition.

Situations, working practices, and conditions

System developers must understand the relations between the following:

- The situations which arise in the project.
- The working practices which are applied in the project.
- The conditions which affect the course of the project.

There is a constant interplay between situations, working practices, and conditions

So far different types of situations have been treated in an isolated way. But situations are products of working practices and conditions. At the same time many situations offer a good opportunity to reassess the way the project is organized, as well as the environment.

A project group was discussing design proposals with a group of users. But the discussions were not very fruitful. The users found it hard to relate to the descriptions presented to them. The situation was problematic because the system developers needed the comments and acceptance of the users. The reason for the problem was that the system developers had employed a specific working practice which resulted in very technical descriptions. The only way to establish real communication with the users was to introduce a new working practice. Figure 2.2 illustrates the interaction between working practices and situations.

In another project, work had come to a standstill. This was an extremely unpleasant situation as the time schedule was very tight, and it happened at the beginning of the project. The project group had submitted the overall design to the steering committee for approval, but several weeks had passed with no answer. The situation reflected the working practices and the conditions. It turned out that there was a fundamental disagreement in the user organization about the requirements of the new system. The user representatives in the steering committee did not have sufficient competence to make decisions. That

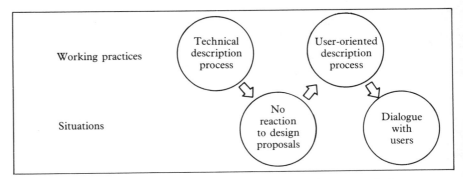

Figure 2.2   The situation is determined by the working practice applied.
However, many situations are good opportunities for trying to
influence the working practice.

was why it took so long to discuss the project group's overall design
proposal. When the positive answer finally came through, the project
group decided to intervene — simply because it was no longer possible
to meet the time schedule. Firstly they changed the working practice:
they decided to give less priority to the analyses which were to form
the basis of the detailed design of a specific part of the system. Instead
they started directly on the detailed design of the remaining part of the
system. Secondly, they changed the conditions: they informed the user
representatives in the steering committee that only part of the system
would be completed on time. In this way they affected the user
organization's expectations of the project. Figure 2.3 illustrates the
interaction between conditions, working practices, and situations. The
working practice of the steering committee is described as part of the
project's working practices. In other situations a project group might
choose to describe the steering committee's working practice as a
condition.

System development projects always interact with the environment.
Conditions affect the course of the project, and it might become
necessary to influence these conditions. Some of the more typical
conditions are listed in Figure 2.4. In practice it is always necessary
to look at the specific conditions of the individual project.

Projects are contractual arrangements

A project is a temporary organizational unit with specific goals. The
various groups of people in a project are linked together in a network

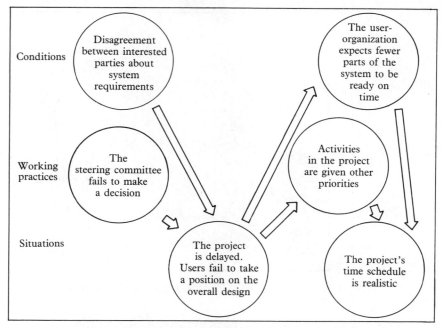

Figure 2.3   Conditions and working practices determine the situations arising in the project. However, many situations are good opportunities for trying to influence both working practices and conditions.

- The assignment.
- Other objectives.
- Interested parties.
- Relation to the user organization.
- Standards, regulations, and agreements.
- Equipment.
- Staff assigned to the project.

Figure 2.4   Some of the important conditions of a systems development project.

of commitments. At the same time a project typically cuts across other, more stable units. The organization in which the new system is to be applied is called the user organization. The primary interest of the user organization is linked to the product to be produced by the project. The organization in which the project takes place is called the development organization. The primary interest of the development organization is linked to the process the project will go through.

The task is assigned. A project is a temporary organizational unit with specific goals.

A project is affected by a number of conditions, and it will consume a number of resources — the most important of which are manpower and equipment. The project will produce various intermediate products and services. The primary result of the project is a computer system and a changed user organization, but the project also results in changed conditions and in increased experience.

Formal and real organization

Many projects are based on a formal project organization consisting of a project group, a steering committee, and, in some cases, a number of reference groups. A project group leader and a chairman of the steering committee are typically appointed formally. The formal project organization can be of major practical importance, but there will often be other things which link the project together as an organizational unit.

Projects take place in real organizations where financial conditions and personal relations play a decisive role. One way to understand a project as an organizational unit is to look at the mutual commitments which link the project participants to each other. These are called mutual commitments contracts. The project contracts determine commitments between people and groups across other organizational arrangements. The contracts determine the products and services one party is committed to deliver, and the corresponding commitments of the other party.

The following are examples of contracts in a system development project:

- Requirement specifications containing the results of the negotiations between the user and development organizations as to what the new system should be.

- The project plan specifying the resources made available to the project group by the development organization. The project group is committed to develop the system on the basis of the stipulations in the project plan.

- The internal division of labour in the project group reflecting how the members commit each other in relation to the assignment.

The examples indicate that these contracts can be of a more or less formal nature. Informal contracts will be found between people who share a common goal. Contracts will become increasingly formal with growing conflicts of interests between the parties. The nature of the contracts also depends on how difficult it is to measure the performance of the involved parties. Contracts link the project group members together as a group, and they regulate the project's relations to the environment.

Product contracts, process contracts, and internal contracts
There are three types of project contracts: product contracts, process contracts, and internal contracts in the product group. Product contracts deal with the characteristics of the new system. An example is a requirement specification or a list of criteria for the users to apply when testing the delivered system. Process contracts deal with the process leading to the desired product. Examples are the overall time schedule or a specification of the manpower needed to ensure that the process leads to the desired product. Product or process contracts between the project group on the one hand and the user or development organization on the other hand are project contracts that regulate the project group's relations with the surrounding world.

Contracts linking the project group together as a group in relation to the assignment are called internal contracts. Internal contracts (for instance module design, project charter, and detailed plans) affect the working practices of a project in a direct way. An important part of the work in the project consists of establishing and regulating these contracts. The examples of internal contracts mentioned above are all formal contracts, but the informal contracts are just as important. They deal with values, norms, and special relations which may be decisive for the way the project is established. These informal contracts are maintained and changed through personal and professional relations throughout the project.

A lot of effort is spent on establishing and regulating contracts

A closer look will now be taken at the activities necessary for establishing and regulating the contracts. They are the activities which link the project together, and they take place between the user organization and the development organization, between the project group and the surrounding world, and between the individual participants in the project group. One can distinguish between the following four types of activities:

- Identifying and contacting the parties involved in the contract.
- Negotiating the contract.
- Controlling whether the contractual partner observes the contract.
- Maintaining the contract.

Type of activity	Overall design (product contract)	Project charter (internal contract)
Search	Finding those users who are going to participate in determining the system's properties.	Finding the project group members.
Negotiation	Informal and formal talks, meetings and written communication about the design.	Discussions of, and decisions on, how the project should be designed, and who is responsible for which tasks.
Control	User test of completed system.	Status meetings in the project group, where the actual course of the project is compared to the project charter.
Maintenance	Informal and formal meetings, where the overall design is discussed and interpreted, and where questions are raised as all the involved parties learn more. May result in renegotiations.	The project work and other professional and private activities maintaining the values, social relations, and commitments keeping the project group together.

Table 2.2   Examples of contracts and of the activities through which they are established and regulated.

If the project is perceived in terms of contracts and ensuing activities — search, negotiation, control, and maintenance — it is realized that it is insufficient to rely on the formal organization. The contractual way of thinking implies that system developers spend time and effort on keeping the project together as a working organizational unit. Some contracts require negotiation, others can be established quickly on the basis of tradition. Some contracts require almost no maintenance, others are very frail. Table 2.2 illustrates two project contracts and their related activities.

Consultant or supplier?

The relation between the user organization and the development organization is one of the most important conditions of a project. At one extreme the development of the system takes place in close cooperation between the two organizations. In cases like that the development organization acts as a consultant for the user organization. At the other extreme cooperation between the two organizations is limited to a minimum. In cases like that the development organization acts as a supplier in relation to the user organization. (See Table 2.3).

The role of consultant is mostly seen in companies which have their own software department, while the role of supplier is the more common in companies which employ a software house.

The supplier delivers a technical system

A supplier relation is typically characterized by the following conditions and assumptions:

- The user organization and the development organization negotiate the contract before the project starts. Frequent checks are made to ensure that the terms of the contract are observed, and breach of contract requires formal negotiations between the two parties.

- The product contract clearly describes the requirements of the new system, as well as the date of delivery and the price.

- The development organization and the project group negotiate the process contract within the stipulations of the product contract. Observation of the process contract is checked internally in the development department.

- The project group does not undertake any, or only minimal, analysis of the user organization.

- Project work consists of detailed design and realization of a computer

Supplier	Consultant
The starting point is a precisely formulated product contract.	The starting point is an open-ended project contract.
Static contracts with few negotiations between development and user organization.	Dynamic contracts with direct negotiations between the project group and the user organization.
Minimal analysis of the user organization.	Analysis of the user organization plays an important role.
The project group produces a computer system.	The project group produces a computer system and cooperates with the user organization when the system is integrated.
The user organization is responsible for integrating the system.	

Table 2.3   In the extremes a project may act either as a supplier or as a consultant in relation to the user organization. Reality usually lies somewhere between.

system consisting of hardware and software, and facilities for handling input and output.

- The user organization is responsible for integrating the computer system. If the project group participates, the procedure for doing so is stipulated in the original contract.

The supplier is responsible for constructing a computer system on the basis of given requirements, given resources, and within given deadlines.

The consultant cooperates in developing a technical and social system

A consultant relation is typically characterized by the following conditions and assumptions:

- The project is based on a project contract containing ideas about the product and the course of the project.

- The project group and development organization on one hand, and the user organization on the other, negotiate both the product and the process contract. Frequent checks are made to ensure that the terms of the contract are observed, and the contract can be renegotiated.

- The project group undertakes analysis of the user organization.

- The project group presents several design proposals which they negotiate with the user organization.

- Project work consists of realizing a computer system and changing the user organization.

- The user organization and the project group cooperate when the system is integrated in the user organization.

Reality usually lies somewhere between the two extremes. But the more the project's basic contracts commit the project to play the role of the supplier, the more will the course of the project be characterized by formalities, and the project group will in reality be cut off from a dialogue with the users. Many projects work like that, and put great demand on the system developers. They must be imaginative and experienced to be able to understand what the system's future use is going to be. They must also be able to cooperate with the salesmen and consultants who have entered into contracts with the client on behalf of the project.

2.4 User participation

The application of computer technology affects fundamental conditions in the user organization

The user organization has a basic interest in controlling the results of a system development project. However, there are often conflicting requirements linked to the computer application. The application of computers affects fundamental aspects like productivity, employment, structure of qualifications, division of labour, and the work environment. Different interest groups and different departments in the user organization will therefore try to influence system development projects with their viewpoints and with the resources available to them.

User participation is not only a question of how and to what extent the user organization exercises its influence. A system development project is an opportunity for different and conflicting interests and attitudes to come into the open. Interest groups and individuals will try to influence the course of the project through negotiation, manipulation, and exercise of legitimate authority. A system development project is often characterized by conflicting interests among the users of the future system. This is manifested in conflicting priorities and decisions.

System developers have a professional interest in seeing that the future users influence the project. The systems developed are often highly integrated in the organization. They play an increasingly important role in the overall function of the organization. System developers need to cooperate with people who know and master the situations and problems related to the new system. At the same time the design proposals and the new system must be acceptable to the user organization.

The importance of the relationship to the user organization varies from project to project. If the project acts as a consultant, there will be direct relations between the various user groups and the project group. If, on the other hand, the project group acts as a supplier, they are often cut off from real cooperation with the various user groups. Hence, not all user demands for participation can or should be incorporated into the project group's working practices. It is, however, useful for system developers to know something about user participation. This kind of knowledge may contribute to lowering the level of frustration in projects subjected to actively interested users. At the same time it may help the members of the project group consider the disadvantages of their own working practices in situations where users and their unions attempt to defend and promote their interests concerning computer technology.

*Professional
and democratic
viewpoints*

System developers are professionally committed to observing the regulations and agreements which regulate the application of computer technology in organizations. Environment acts, technology agreements, etc., contain different types of guidelines for applying computer technology such as the following:

- Guidelines which directly state that employees must be able to exercise influence.

- Guidelines concerning information to employees.

- Guidelines concerning training of employees.

- Guidelines stating that management must make resources available to the labour organizations.

- Guidelines indicating how the systems should be designed.

These guidelines make demands on the relation between a project group and the user organization. These demands concern who is to participate, in what way, when, and where, during the course of the project. Figure 2.5 illustrates examples of formulations from selected Scandinavian laws and agreements.

Section 2.   The parties agree that management is responsible for informing the
              employees of introduction and application of new, as well as changes in
              existing technology.
  Subsection 2.   Information must be submitted in writing for discussion in a
                   joint committee and/or in an, according to Section 3,
                   appointed technology committee.
  Subsection 3.   Information must be submitted early enough to allow for
                   thorough discussions, so that the viewpoints of the employees
                   form part of management's consideratons and decisions.
  Subsection 4.   Information must concern
                   A.   The new technology's
                        a. objectives,
                        b. function,
                        c. design,
                        d. economy, and
                        e. connections to other systems.
                   B.   The expected consequences of the above concerning
                        a. work environment,
                        b. organization and content of work,
                        c. staff requirements,
                        d. use of staff, including allocation of jobs, and
                        e. training.

                              (Technology agreement, public sector, Denmark)

Section 5.3.4. Employees must together with their shop stewards participate in the
                design or further development of computer systems in their companies if
                they are or will be directly affected by them.

Section 5.3.5. When employees or their shop stewards participate in a concrete project,
                they must have access to all documents concerning the project. They can
                require that alternative solutions be presented and explained.

                              (Technology agreement, public sector, Section 5 of Main
                              Agreement, Norway)

Section 11.   Before management makes a decision concerning important changes, they
              must take initiative to local negotiations . . .

                              (Act of Participation, Sweden)

Figure 2.5   Regulations and agreements are important conditions for the
             development and use of computer technology. The quotations are
             from selected Scandinavian regulations and agreements.

Wishes and demands concerning user participation are not only
expressed in regulations and agreements. Most important is the concrete
initiatives taken by various groups in connection with the individual
project. Several projects have seen users and their unions require
technology assessments, and initiatives like that may affect the course
of the project. Generally such initiatives make demands on descriptions
and tests. They will typically require that a so-called unbiased third

party has the opportunity to assess design proposals and pilot systems. Also the project might get delayed because more time is needed for assessments, discussions, and negotiations.

System developers are professionally forced to take an interest in the relations to the users, the user organization, and the unions. They must know the requirements, possibilities, and problems connected to this fundamental aspect of systems development. If system developers also wish to contribute to a democratization of systems development, they must work for transparency in the projects. From a democratic viewpoint they should aim at the following:

- Informing affected people and groups of results and status.

- Making their information such that everyone understands it.

- Pointing out alternative options, where the chosen alternative is uncertain, or where other alternatives could be chosen.

- Pointing out the reasoning and assumptions on which the choices are based.

- Clarifying and motivating the chosen procedures.

2.5 To change working practices

Death to standard methods

Each system development method tries to present a well-organized and comprehensive picture of the work in a project. But practice confronts the system developers with many different types of situations requiring completely different types of action. Therefore, death to standard methods.

Professional systems development requires two things. First, it requires active and competent management of the individual project. The project should be established systematically, plans should be kept up to date, status should be re-evaluated, and working practices and basic conditions should be changed if necessary. Secondly, professional systems development requires that the system developers are willing and able to change and develop their repertoire of working practices.

Almost all development organizations know that it is necessary to invest resources in changing working practices. But the resources are

Routine. In routine situations the problem and the task are known, and the system developer knows which working practices to apply. But system developers cannot rely on routine alone.

often spent in an inefficient manner. What is the use of a methods department if the methods it develops are not applied in practice?

Changing working practices is certainly not easy. It is necessary to shake up attitudes and traditions. It is necessary to invest sufficient resources. And last, but not least, it is necessary to anchor the innovative activity in the individual projects because that is where the dynamic energies are, and that is where the opportunities to turn new ideas into reality can be found.

You can read more about changing working practices in other parts of the book. Part II of the book (Chapters 4 to 10) suggests a number of working practices which the professional system developer should master. Part III (Chapters 11 to 13) discusses how the introduction of new working practices can be organized in a development organization.

Further reading

The arguments against the rational model in Section 2.1 are based on Parnas and Clements (1985). The division into routine, problem solving, and problem setting, and the discussion of uncertainty in Section 2.2, is based on Lanzara (1983). The discussion of the contractual concept in Section 2.3 is inspired by Ouchi (1980) and Ciborra (1981). The discussion of technology agreements is based on Mathiassen *et al.* (1983), while the requirements of system developers who wish to participate in a democratization process in systems development is based on Ehn and Sandberg (1979).

3 What is systems development?

Professionalism is also based on theory

Experience plays the leading part in practical systems development. Nothing will change that. Some system developers, however, rely on only their own experience — they fail to exploit the inspiration and experience of other people. Consequently they repeat mistakes which could have been avoided. They fail to see new possibilities. They find it hard to explain to themselves and to others why one choice is better than another, or why specific problems or conflicts surface in the project.

The professional system developer is open-minded towards the experience of other people. The professional system developer learns from cooperating with others and from studying methods and theories on systems development. Methods are merely prescriptions based on experience. A method is practical because it gives guidelines for how specific tasks should be approached. Methods are, however, no longer practical when the situation fails to meet the method's guidelines. In situations like this additional comprehensive knowledge is needed; theories are needed.

Methods and theories can never replace experience; but new methods may inspire experienced practitioners, and theories may help them understand and process their own experience.

This is the most theoretical chapter of the book. At the same time this chapter contains a summary of the principles presented in the book. If the reader so wishes, it is possible to skip through Chapter 3 and then return to it after studying the rest of the book.

The chapter presents a number of concepts to help understand what systems development is. The main emphasis is laid on the development process and its components. Section 3.1 discusses the application of computer technology in organizations. Section 3.2 looks at the main components of systems development and at some basic principles. Section 3.3 presents four different views on the type of process dealt with: a process of cognition, a process of innovation, a process of construction, and a political process. Finally Section 3.4 discusses the relationship between methods and working practices.

3.1 Computer technology in organizations

Development and use of computer systems are intrinsically related activities

One may look at computer technology in organizations in two different, complementary ways. One way is to look at how the technology is used: the focus is then on the computer-based systems in the organization. Another way is to look at how applications are developed: the focus is then on systems development in the organization.

The nature of the applications keeps changing. Those days are over when computer technology primarily was applied to automate well-known manual routines. Today computer technology is increasingly spread and integrated in the individual organizations. The technology is applied in several areas. It is embedded in existing equipment and hardware, and many systems which used to stand alone are now linked together through networks in complex computer-based systems.

The technological basis is also changing. There has been a drastic decrease in the cost of equipment, and this has made it feasible to spread the equipment throughout the organization and to dedicate it to individual applications. Linking systems and equipment together has become less complicated and less expensive. New types of display screens have made it possible to handle information on the electronic media in a way which allows for the habits and techniques we have developed with paper as the primary medium. Figure 3.1 outlines the changes in equipment and the accompanying changes in the systems development process.

These changes imply that new demands are made on systems development efforts. New technological, organizational, and specific professional knowledge must be present. Projects will no longer typically end up with completely new computer-based systems. The projects will just as often work with modifications or additions to existing applications. The development processes have traditionally preceded the applications. But the individual application is now typically applied for a time, then it is developed further to be applied in a changed form for a while, and so on.

Computer system and computer-based system

Systems development is now part of organizational development and it is increasingly turning into a political process. Not only is the process characterized by technical and financial issues, it also includes

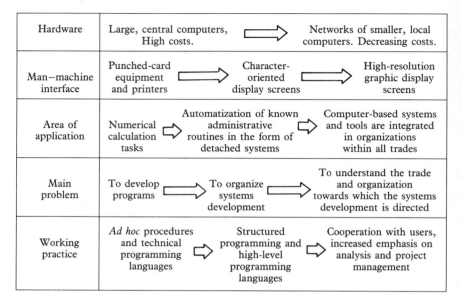

Hardware	Large, central computers, High costs.	→	Networks of smaller, local computers. Decreasing costs.
Man–machine interface	Punched-card equipment and printers	Character-oriented display screens →	High-resolution graphic display screens
Area of application	Numerical calculation tasks	Automatization of known administrative routines in the form of detached systems →	Computer-based systems and tools are integrated in organizations within all trades
Main problem	To develop programs	To organize systems development →	To understand the trade and organization towards which the systems development is directed
Working practice	*Ad hoc* procedures and technical programming languages	Structured programming and high-level programming languages →	Cooperation with users, increased emphasis on analysis and project management

Figure 3.1 An outline of some of the development traits linked to systems development.

broad organizational questions. The product is not only a technical system, but also an organizational change affecting working practices, and social and technological issues. That is why we make a distinction between computer systems and computer-based systems. A computer system consists of program executions, hardware, software, and data. A computer system is developed to handle specific subfunctions in the organization. A computer-based system includes a computer system, but also those parts of the organization which contribute to or depend upon the same function as the computer system.

Systems development includes both modification of existing computer-based systems and development of new ones. The overall systems development process in an organization is directed at all the computer-based systems in the organization. A systems development project is limited in time and is directed at a specific part of the organization's computer-based systems.

3.2 Performance and management

We need method-independent descriptions of systems development

What components is systems development made up of? What type of work is involved? All systems development methods contain an answer to that, but the answers are always linked directly to the guidelines in the books. A method-independent understanding of systems development is needed. How would it otherwise be possible to understand and explain the actual situations in a project? Or how would systematic comparison be possible between different methods?

There are various possibilities for characterizing the main components of systems development:

- The work itself can be described, or the services and products resulting from the work can be described.

- What actually happens can be described, or what is intended to happen.

- The descriptions can be made more or less abstract.

Here the work itself is chosen as the starting point. Figure 3.2 illustrates some basic concepts for this purpose. Function, task, activity, and process correspond to more or less abstract ways of looking at work, and they describe both what actually happens, and what is intended to happen.

Process and activity

A process is the most concrete description of what actually happens. Processes take place in time and space, and they can be split up into sub-processes. A systems development project contains a process limited in time, resulting in specific products and services.

An activity denotes selected parts of a process which are seen as belonging together, for instance interviewing user groups, programming a module, or revising detailed plans. Activities denote what is actually done in a systems development project. However, a description of an activity is more abstract than a description of the process itself. In an activity specific aspects of the elements in the process have been selected.

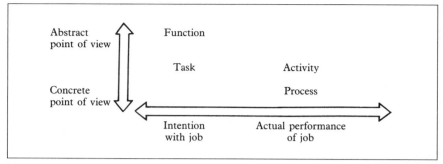

Figure 3.2   Some basic concepts for describing systems development.

The name of the activity typically indicates those elements in the process which is focused on. A project group meeting may be seen as a process where various events take place simultaneously; presenting viewpoints, discussing, passing on information, drinking coffee, etc. The meeting may be viewed in a more abstract way, namely as an activity: a review. In that case the interest is in the specific aspects of the process linked to this activity — others are ignored.

Function and task

A function is the most abstract way of looking at systems development. As opposed to processes and activities which express what is actually happening, a function denotes the intended result of one or more processes regardless of how the processes actually take place. Analysis, design, and planning are examples of functions which in practice correspond to specific activities. Functions, like activities, are delimited by content and thus activities typically contribute to the execution of the corresponding function. A function is performed through one or more activities. One may talk about the function of planning or about the activity of planning. The relationship between functions and processes is more vague because processes are not delimited by content, but rather denote the totality of what actually takes place in the course of a project. Thus a process typically contributes to several functions simultaneously. A process might, for instance, contribute to both analysis and design activities.

A task is a more concrete description of an intention. A function can typically be concretized into a number of tasks directly indicating the desired result. The planning function may, for instance, be concretized in: working out the next baseline, working out a detailed plan for the next phase, revising an overall project plan, etc. The tasks may correspond directly to the equivalent activities.

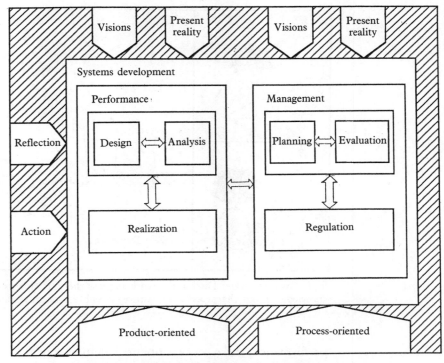

Figure 3.3 The main components of systems development. On the
functional level the arrows indicate the relation between
funtions. On the activity level the arrows indicate the
interaction between activities.

It is time to leave the basic concepts and move on to what all this
is really about: the main components of systems development. The
description given in Figure 3.3 is based on three fundamental
distinctions:

- Product orientation versus process orientation.
- Reflection versus action.
- Present realities versus visions.

Performance and management

System developers basically perform two types of creative activities.
They create a computer-based system, i.e. a computer system and
changes in the user organization. And they create a project resulting
in the planned computer-based system. Systems development thus
consists of two elements: a product-oriented element which we call

Reflection and action. During the work process the participants develop new knowledge about the process: its nature, possible procedures and possible tools.

Reflection and action

performance, and a process-oriented element which we call management.

Apart from this distinction a distinction is made between reflective activities and actions. Systems development requires an organizational, as well as a technical understanding of possibilities and conditions. However, the basic intention is to create and to change. The interaction between reflection and action takes place all through the course of the project, for instance when a module is to be designed and realized, or when an activity is to be planned and carried out.

Present realities and visions

Finally a distinction is made between two types of reflective activities: reflections directed at present realities, and reflections directed at future possibilities. To act consciously one must understand the starting point, and at the same time be able to visualize in what direction one wishes to move.

Figure 3.3 illustrates the main components of systems development based on the above-mentioned distinctions. The components may be seen both as functions and as activities. Seen as functions the arrows indicate the relationship between functions. Seen as activities the arrows indicate the interaction between activities. Irrespective of what viewpoint is chosen, the figure stresses that the main components of systems development partly consist of analysis, design, realization, evaluation, planning, and regulation; and partly of the relation between these. In any project the specific content of the individual activities and their interaction is concretized and tied in time and space. Correspondingly a method contains a number of suggestions for how this should be done.

The advantage of this abstract description of the main components of systems development is that it is not connected to a specific project model. It emphasizes limitations and options, and it can be employed to evaluate and compare both specific projects and selected methods. The weakness of this abstract description is that it disregards the fact that systems development is enacted in an interaction between many people who, among other things, do not share the same interests, do not have the same resources at their disposal, and do not have the same qualifications. These aspects will be discussed later in this book.

Performance

The actual performance of systems development — the product-oriented part — consists of the reflective functions (analysis and design) and of the innovative function (realization).

Analysis leads to an understanding of present realities

The analysis function is directed at present realities — the user organization, technical options, and existing design proposals. The analysis function results in an understanding of the user organization, of technical possibilities, and of design proposals. The analysis function is typically carried out in activities such as the following:

- Interviewing users on their current practices.
- Describing working processes.
- Describing data flows.
- Visiting other organizations to study similar systems.
- Describing technical options.
- Evaluating design proposals.

Design leads to visions of the future

The design function is directed at future technical and organizational possibilities. The design function includes formulation of one or several visions of a desired change in the user organization. The design function results in descriptions of programs, computer systems, and working processes. The design function is typically carried out in activities such as the following:

- Meetings where ideas are generated.

- Working out tenders.
- Describing functions.
- Description of module structure.
- Overall description of modules.
- Determining system architecture.
- Describing working processes.

Realization leads to actual changes

The realization function is directed at the computer equipment and at the user organization. The realization function results in programs and computer systems, and in changed working practices, qualifications, and attitudes in the user organization. The realization function is typically carried out in activities such as the following:

- Coding programs.
- Integrating and testing programs.
- Implementing new or modified computer systems.
- Changing work organization.
- Training users.
- Conversion.

Performance principles

There are a number of basic characteristics linked to analysis, design, and realization. In the following these characteristics will be formulated in the form of a number of principles. The first principles are linked to the relations or the interaction between analysis, design, and realization (see Figures 3.4 and 3.5).

Principle P1: Analysis and design are mutually dependent, and should therefore be performed concurrently in order to support each other.

Understanding the relevant parts of the user organization and the technological possibilities is a prerequisite for being able to make design realistic. And visions of the technical and organizational change is a prerequisite for being able to delimit the area of analysis and formulate the criteria according to which the relevance of the analysis activity is determined. The logical sequence of first analysis followed by design is often preferred. In practice, however, it is impossible to perform analysis activities without having visions of the new system.

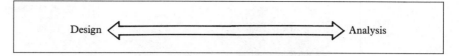

Figure 3.4 The relation between design and analysis.

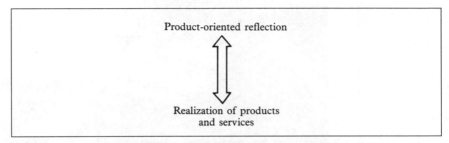

Figure 3.5 The relation between product-oriented reflection and realization of products and services.

Principle P2:   Product oriented reflection (analysis and design) and realization affect each other, and should therefore be performed concurrently in order to support each other.

Understanding the starting point and the desired change is a prerequisite for being able to organize and realize the actual change. And concrete experience gained through the realization activities creates a need for new analyses and designs. The logical sequence here is: first analysis and design, then realization. Test situations in practice will, however, always disclose problems which require renewed analysis or design considerations. It might be a question of errors in the system, but also of constructive suggestions for alternative solutions.

The logical sequence of analysis and design followed by realization can be observed as the main direction in practical systems development (see Figure 3.6). In the beginning of a project emphasis will naturally be on analysis, and as the project moves on, the emphasis will shift to design, and later to realization.

Leave room for moving against the main direction

The two principles mentioned above point towards a piece of practical advice: organize the project so that there is room for moving against the main direction in systems development. This will add insight which will increase efficiency and improve the quality of the product.

Figure 3.6   The main direction in systems development.

Planning a test, for instance, is not enough. New analysis, design, and realization activities emanating from the test must also be planned.

So far we have tried to understand the process. But what about the results? Table 3.1 gives an outline of the relation between analysis, design, and realization on the one hand, and the intended results and relations to project contracts on the other hand. In practice the big challenge is to realize these relations with due consideration to efficiency and quality.

Chapters 8, 9, and 10 will discuss analysis, design, and realization. These chapters discuss the following principles concerning the actual performance of systems development:

Principle P3:   It is not possible to perform qualified analysis and design strictly according to given guidelines.

Function	Intended results	Intended relation to project contract
Analysis	• Description of the user organization. • Description and evaluation of technical possibilities. • Evaluation of design proposals.	• Forms the basis of creating and changing the product contract. • Contains evaluation of product contracts.
Design	• Overall design. • Functional design. • Technical design.	• Results in product contracts. • Consists of clarification and refinement of the product contract. • Input to creation of process contracts
Realization	• Programs, computer systems. • Changed working practices, qualifications, and attitudes in the user organization.	• Subject to product contracts. • May lead to re-negotiations of product contracts.

Table 3.1 The relation between subfunctions during performance on the one hand and intended relations to results and product contracts on the other.

	The activities require experience, intuition, imagination, and reflection.
Principle P4:	The project group's relation to the users is of decisive importance to the quality of the analysis. If direct cooperation cannot be established between developers and users, precise requirement specifications and knowledge about the application situation are needed.
Principle P5:	Good design is a question of flying high — and keeping both feet firmly on the ground. New visions and unconventional solutions must be created. It must at the same time be possible to introduce them into the organization.

Principle P6:   Technically oriented analysis and design may result in perfect solutions to the wrong problems. Qualified analysis and design require technical, organizational and social competence.

Principle P7:   Qualified analysis and design require that different perspectives are applied. The choice of techniques and tools, and the choice of how to organize the process depend upon the situation.

Principle P8:   Neither the analysis nor the design activities can move unidirectionally from totality to detail. Knowledge of details and of the concrete conditions are prerequisites for obtaining a comprehensive view of the situation.

Principle P9:   Tests do not solve any problems. Plan with time for repairs, thus preventing permanent fire-fighting.

Principle P10:   Qualified realization requires thorough planning of the conversion. The overall design should include the conversion plan.

Management

Consider now the management of system development projects — the process-oriented part — which consists of the reflective functions: evaluation and planning, and of the innovative function: regulation. See Figure 3.3.

Evaluation leads to understanding of the situation

The evaluation function is directed at the process itself, and at the current plans. The evaluaton function results in an understanding of the applied working practices and the prevailing conditions of the project. The evaluation function also leads to assessments of the distance between the project's current status and current plans, and it leads to identification of errors, problems, and conflicts linked to the project. The evaluation function is typically carried out in activities such as the following:

• Assessment of status.
• Evaluation of plans.

- Evaluation of meetings.
- Evaluation of progress.
- Reporting to the development and user organizations.

Planning leads to visions about the course of the project

The planning function is directed at future working practices and future conditions of the project. The planning function results in plans on various levels, and in a description of the conditions constituting the prerequisites of realizing the plan. The planning function is typically carried out in activities such as the following:

- Establishing the project.
- Overall planning.
- Detailed planning.

Regulation results in changes

The regulation function is directed at the process in a broad sense. The regulation function is directed at the participants' expectations, attitudes, and qualifications, at working practices in the project, and at the conditions of the project. The regulation function results in changes in the process, and is typically carried out in activities such as the following:

- Establishing the project.
- Project group meetings.
- Negotiations with the development and user organizations.
- Evaluation activities.
- Courses and training.

Management principles

A number of basic principles are linked to management of system development projects. The first of these deal with the relation or interaction between evaluation, planning, and regulation (see Figures 3.7 and 3.8), and they correspond to the equivalent principles on performance.

Principle M1:   Evaluation and planning are mutually dependent, and should therefore be performed concurrently in order to support each other.

Having insight into the project and knowing the relation between the project and current plans is, on the one hand, a prerequisite for

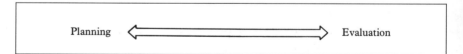

Figure 3.7 The relation between planning and evaluation.

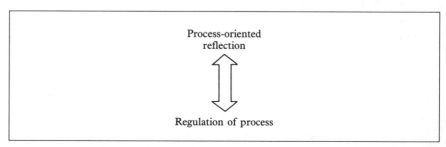

Figure 3.8 The relation between process-oriented reflection and regulation of the process.

being able to make realistic plans. Plans, on the other hand, are a prerequisite for being able to delimit and direct the evaluation of the project. In other words: idealistic plans merely collect dust on the shelves, and project evaluations with no relation to the objectives of the project seldom find a willing ear.

Principle M2:	Process-oriented reflection (planning and evaluation) and regulation affect each other, and should therefore be performed concurrently in order to support each other.

Understanding and accepting both the planned and the actual course of the project is a prerequisite for being able to regulate the project in the required direction. And concrete experience with regulating the course of the project creates a need for new evaluation and planning activities. In other words, it is unwise to act in the dark, and it is naive to think that it is possible to see all the options and consequences from the outset when the project is planned.

Table 3.2 illustrates the interaction between management functions on the one hand and the intended results and relations to the project contracts on the other.

Chapters 4, 5, 6, and 7 will discuss management of systems development projects. This is an extensive and important field of study, and the chapters do not attempt to give an exhaustive presentation. However, the selected subjects will emphasize and illuminate the following principles concerning management of projects:

Principle M3:	Systems development is characterized by a high degree of uncertainty. The most important prerequisite for qualified management is therefore transparency in both processes and products.
Principle M4:	It pays to establish the project systematically.
Principle M5:	Baselines and checkpoints are better than traditional phases. Traditional division into phases confuses time and content, thus making dynamic regulation of the project difficult.
Principle M6:	Project plans must facilitate evaluations. They must be in writing and contain evaluation criteria and procedures.

Function	Intended results	Intended relations to project contracts
Evaluation	• Understanding working practices and conditions. • Evaluation of distance between plans and status. • Identification of errors, problems, and conflicts.	• Forms the basis of creating and changing the process contract • Evaluation of the process contract
Planning	• Plans on different levels. • Description of conditions required by the plan.	• Based on the product contract. • Results in the process contract. • Consists of clarification and refinement of the process contract.
Regulation	• Changed working practices. • Changed qualifications, attitudes, and expectations of participants. • Changed conditions for the project, including changed contracts.	• Subject to the process contract. • May result in re-negotiation of the process contract. • Affects internal contracts.

Table 3.2   The interaction between management functions on the one hand and the intended results and relations to the project contracts on the other.

Principle M7:   Only the system developers know enough to make realistic plans and to evaluate the status of the project.

Principle M8:   It is important that all participants in a project understand and accept the plan.

Principle M9.   It is necessary to apply several estimation techniques. The plan should be based on a probable estimate, and express the degree of uncertainty in the estimate.

Principle M10:   It is necessary to plan with management activities. Management typically constitutes 15% to 25% of the effort.

Management and performance

Systems development is characterized by a high degree of uncertainty

The last, but perhaps most important, component of systems development is the relation between management and performance (see Figure 3.9 and Figure 3.3).

System development projects are typically characterized by a high degree of uncertainty. This is expressed in the following fundamental principle:

Principle PM1: A system development project should be organized in a way which ensures direct and close interaction between performance and management activities.

Unforeseen and problematic situations typically occur during a project. Managing the project effectively therefore requires up to date and thorough insight into the project. Effective management can neither be realized through directives or standards, nor by people who do not themselves participate in the actual performance of the project. In other words: it is impossible to manage system development projects effectively with traditional bureaucratic means.

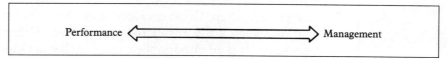

Figure 3.9   The relation between performance and management.

Principle PM2: The most important intermediate products are the plan and the overall design.

There is evidently a strong analogy between performance and management. The plan is the key document in management. The overall design is the key document in performance. Poor management is characterized by poor plans and poor evaluation — and this leads to projects characterized by randomness and confusion. Poor performance is characterized by poor analysis and design — and this easily leads to unnecessary firefighting. If the analogy is carried a little further, it will be seen that project evaluation must identify those areas in the project which require new plans and regulation. Analysis must correspondingly identify those areas in the user organization and in the new system which require new design reflections and intervention.

This analogy may seem artificial on first sight. What is expressed, however, is merely a fundamental view on the elements entering into understanding and changing processes. Performance and management both aim at processes: management at the process in the project, and performance at the process which is the users' work. From this point of view it seems natural to look at performance and management in the same manner.

Decision-making, communication and socialization

General functions

In addition to the characteristic components listed above, there are a number of more general functions. Here decision-making, communication and socialization will be considered. They are functions which appear as important components in most working situations. Figure 3.10 gives an outline of the total set of subfunctions of systems development.

Many decisions are made in a system development project. The decisions deal with both the process and the products, and they influence the project contracts in a broad sense. Some decisions are made internally in the project group. Other decisions involve external groups and people. Some decisions are a result of negotiations. Others are a result of cooperation. It is an important experience that decisions may take time,

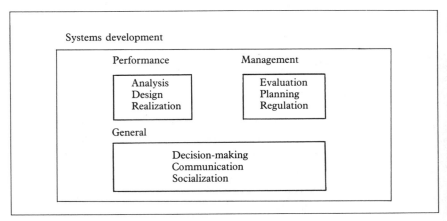

Figure 3.10   The subfunctions of systems development.

and that they may delay the project. A good plan takes this fact into consideration.

Communication is a necessary and decisive function simply because a system development project involves the participation of several people. Communication may be characterized by its content, form, and location in relation to the project. The content of communication deals with the project contracts in a broad sense — it deals with both the process and the products. The location of communication depends on the sender and the receiver: whether, for instance, the communication takes place between people or groups who both work in the project, or whether only one of the parties works with systems development. The form of communication depends on the language and the medium applied, and on whether the communication is one-way or a dialogue. It is an important experience that communication problems are often severe. One of the reasons for this is that computer technology requires formalized descriptions which differ from everyday language.

Socialization is also a decisive function simply because several people participate in the project. Socialization first and foremost takes place when the project is established, on project group meetings, and through the social processes in the project. The socialization function is primarily directed at the project's internal and informal contracts. It is a common mistake that the socialization function is given low priority. This may lead to serious problems in relation to both results and activities. Management activities must therefore be designed to contribute to the performance of this subfunction.

Exercise 3.1

Discuss the subfunctions in a project

Analyse the last project in whch you participated.

- How much emphasis was given to the various subfunctions?

- How did the interaction between the subfunctions work?

- Could some of the problems, errors, or conflicts in the project have been handled better by performing the subfunctions differently?

> **Exercise 3.2**
>
> **Discuss the subfunctions in a method**
>
> Analyse one of the methods described in the literature or in the project handbook of your company.
>
> • How are the various subfunctions weighted?
>
> • How is the interaction between the subfunctions described?
>
> • What types of problems, errors, and conflicts is the method poor at handling?

3.3 Views on systems development

So far this chapter has presented a number of concepts and fundamental principles for understanding and handling systems development processes. You could say that system developers often know a lot about what they are working with, but rarely very much about their work. That is why they find it difficult to discuss and exchange experience, and to let new methods affect their traditional working practices.

This section will look at the systems development process from various viewpoints. Each viewpoint interprets systems development as a specific kind of process. General knowledge about these different types of processes can serve as a base to increase understanding of the problems that typically surface in a project. And a more realistic attitude can be adopted to important conditions and possible working practices.

Construction, change, cognition, and policies

First, systems development can be looked at as a process of construction. The intention is to construct a computer system — and this system is to be integrated in the user organization. Systems development is a kind of organizational development, but it is the aspect of construction which gives the process its specific characteristics. The formalized descriptions necessary for realizing the computer system must live up to strict demands. Insight into the technical equipment to be applied, and into any other systems with relevance for the project, is a prerequisite. The complexity is often so great that systems development not only requires technical insight from its performers, but also that they have a solid talent for abstraction and systematization.

Secondly, systems development can be viewed as a technical and organizational change process. The fundamental intention of a systems development project is to change the technological, formal, and social structures in the user organization. The process itself also requires that structures are established (the project contracts) within the frames of which the process can take place. These structures must be maintained and changed throughout the project. Social innovation processes are basically directed at human beings and human relations. Technologies are, in this connection, only a means. Qualified innovative work requires a good deal of human and organizational insight.

Thirdly, systems development can be viewed as a process of cognition. On the one hand something must be learned about the user organization and about the technical and organizational possibilities for changing it. On the other hand something must be learned about the setting in which the process is to take place, and about the technical and organizational possibilities for designing the project. Processes of cognition cannot be reduced to routine work. They require experiments, an open mind, and inspiration. That is one of the reasons why systems development projects must be organized in a way which ensures close interaction between performing and managing activities.

Fourthly, systems development can be viewed as a political process. The various participating groups and individuals only to a limited degree share a common goal. They see system development projects as an opportunity to promote their own interests, maybe even at the cost of other people's interests. Conflicts which have been hidden so far may surface and affect the project alongside with the already acknowledged conflicts. The political process may take place in an atmosphere of cooperation, of negotiation, or of struggle, depending on what kind of process it is and on the strength of the participating parties. The professional system developer does not try to conceal the political process, but lets it take place in suitable environments.

All these very different characteristics of systems development make it an exciting, but also demanding, discipline. Systems development requires a lot from the individual performer, and it requires effective cooperation between the various individuals and groups.

3.4 Theory, method and working practices

All system developers have a working practice, whereas methods are means they may try to apply. System developers can change their working practice by applying a new method. Working practices can be learned by working with people who have already mastered them. Methods are described, and they can be learned through a combination of study and experiments.

Good methods are formulated as part of a theory

One quality requirement of a method is that it is formulated as part of a theory on systems development. How otherwise would support be found once the situation failed to fit the assumptions on which the method was based? How otherwise could different methods be assessed and compared? This requirement is unfortunately only rarely met in practice. It is true that some methods are based on theories, but they are often theories on the products — the computer systems — and not theories on the process as well.

Systems development method

In the previous sections a theory on systems development has been outlined. Ideally a theory should enable one to understand some of the important laws and mechanisms determining the design and course of a system development project. A method, as opposed to a theory, is directly oriented towards action. A method is prescriptive, and does not give any, or only few, explanations.

Here the choice made is to characterize a systems development method by its area of application, by the underlying perspective, and by the guidelines for the process. A further choice is to distinguish between different types of guidelines: techniques, recommendations of tools, and principles of organization (see Figure 3.11).

- Application area.
- Perspective.
- Guidelines:

  (a) Techniques.
  (b) Tools.
  (c) Principles of organization.

Figure 3.11   Characteristics of systems development methods.

Application area

All systems development methods have a more or less limited area of application. There is quite a difference between automating simple, administrative routines, and developing a computer-integrated manufacturing system. There is also quite a difference between developing an off-line payroll system for 25 employees, and developing an on-line system with 500 terminals allocated in 200 bank branches. This is not only a question of size, but also of differences in important areas, such as the equipment applied, who and how many are participating, the type of organizational change, and how the new system is integrated into the organization's working processes. Different systems development methods have something in common, but it is important that the application area of the individual method is made clear.

Perspective

Any method imposes a specific perspective on its users. The perspective leads to a specific way of seeing, or a specific way of understanding, a given phenomenon, for instance a given organization or organizations as a whole. The perspective of a method is not necessarily described explicitly as part of the method. The perspective is, however, always reflected in the guidelines: for instance in the concepts applied in analysis and design, in the techniques corresponding to these concepts, and in the linguistic means of expression applied for working out descriptions. When you choose and apply a specific method, the perspective of this method also makes you choose a specific fundamental way of looking at the organization, and at the application of computer technology.

A method consists of various guidelines: techniques, recommendations of tools, and principles of organization. The various guidelines are, however, weighted very differently. Some methods are only tools.

Techniques

A technique indicates how a specific working process can be performed: to fish with traps, how to plane wood, how to construct programs through stepwise refinement. A technique focuses on how an activity can be performed. A technique links knowledge of the desired product to an understanding of how the activity should be performed. However, a technique does not take available resources into consideration, nor the setting in which the activity is to be performed. The formulation of a technique often supposes that only one person is involved, and that this person has access to all the necessary resources.

Tools

A technique employs a number of tools: for instance a trap, a plane, a planing bench, a programming language. A tool is constructed as a help to perform a specific type of activity in the most effective way, and as such the tool is linked to one or more techniques. On the one hand the construction of a tool requires the idea of a technique, the application of which is improved by the tool. Applying a new tool, on the other hand, results in new experience, and thus a changed basis for establishing new techniques. For instance, consider the relation between programming techniques and programming languages: in the beginning when programming (the activity) was done directly in machine language, there was a need to develop a conscious attitude (techniques) towards the use of storage units, otherwise things would go wrong. Later, assembler languages were developed (new tool). They made it possible to employ the computer as an aid to administer the use of the physical storage, and at the same time they created the basis for new and different programming experiences. The development of techniques and tools go hand in hand, and together they express a professional knowledge about a specific type of activity and the associated products.

Principles of organization

The principles of organization indicate how the various people and groups should cooperate, and how the always limited resources should be employed and allocated. The principles of organization are seldom directly linked to the individual types of activities. Primarily they indicate the interaction between performance and management. Examples of parts of methods indicating principles of organization are: division into project groups and steering committees, user participation during analysis, division into phases with checkpoints and baselines.

Relationship between method, function and process

This chapter will conclude by illustrating the relationship between some of the central concepts introduced. The relationship is expressed in Figure 3.12.

The function description, expressed in the nine subfunctions, is an abstract description of the systems development process. A function

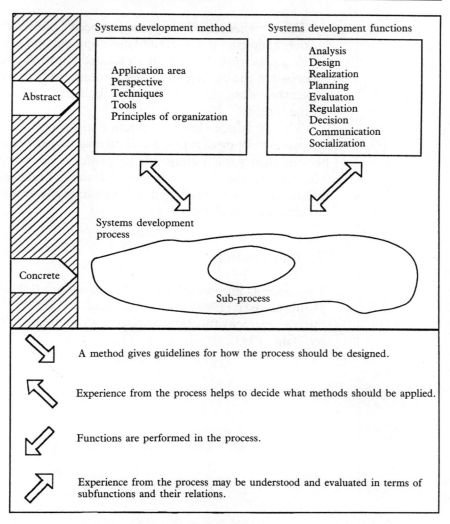

Figure 3.12   This relationship between method, function, and process.

expresses the intention of some of the activities taking place in the process. A function embraces the things required to happen.

A method expresses how activities should be performed. The method gives guidelines for the systems development process. A method indicates which activities can take place simultaneously. A method also indicates the qualifications required to succeed in performing the activities, and it recommends a number of tools.

Finally what actually happens has been captured on a concrete level in the concept: the systems development process. The systems development process may be described through the actual working processes of the participants, and through the actual conditions under which they work. Attention may be focused on a few sub-processes or on the totality.

Theory is one thing — practice quite another. What counts in systems development is practice. This chapter has been rather theoretical because theory is a prerequisite for professional systems development. The rest of this book will present more practical directions and discussions which, it is hoped, will illustrate and amplify the theoretical contents of this chapter.

Further reading

The concepts introduced in this chapter are based on Mathiassen (1981), Munk-Madsen (1984), and Munk-Madsen (1985). The supplement of the management function compared to Mathiassen (1981) is inspired by Dahl (1982).

Part II

Systems Development in Practice

4 Project establishment — a sound investment

Take responsibility for your project

Professional systems development requires active and competent project cultivation throughout the project. That is why the project group must spend time on systematically establishing the project.

Many different groups and individuals have something at stake in a system development project. Each group or individual will try to influence the organization and the course of the project. The concern here, however, is the situation seen from the project group's point of view. The first critical period of the project will be considered: how can the project group prepare itself and develop suitable conditions for handling the problematic and critical situations which will surface later in the project? How can the project group influence the working conditions which are so important to their own professional development and job satisfaction in the period to come?

Section 4.1 discusses why system development projects must be systematically established, and what this activity may include. Section 4.2 looks at some of the typical conditions a project group must analyse and perhaps influence in order to establish and clarify the overall design of the project. Section 4.3 looks at how the project group itself is established. This will include socialization, training, and organization of working practices. Section 4.4 looks at the project charter — one of the major products of project establishment. Section 4.5 concludes this chapter by discussing some of the difficulties which may impede an ideal project establishment.

4.1 Projects must be established

Why must a project be established systematically?

Why is it so important that the project is established systematically? One reason is that this activity contributes to giving the project a realistic starting point: the project is defined by a more or less precise assignment and perhaps on the one hand by a number of other objectives. On the other hand the project is subjected to a number of organizational, financial, and technical conditions. Is the relation between these factors realistic? Or will it be necessary to modify the ambitions or to change the conditions?

A second reason is that project establishment helps the project group to understand and accept the situation they are facing. Maybe the assignment could be formulated in a clearer and more explicit way. The participants might find the opportunity to influence the course of the project. Maybe conditions could be made clearer and perhaps changed. If the participants are to take responsibility for the project, they must know the assignment and the goals in as far as these can be formulated. They must know and accept the project's conditions.

A third reason is that project establishment elucidates and affects the relations between the project and its environment. The project group must understand what is required and expected from them, just as the project's environment must understand the project's requirements and expectations. Environment here means the users and the user organization, management of the development organization, unions, and other projects.

A fourth reason is that project establishment supports the project group itself. Working practices should be considered, and the course of the project must be planned. Training might be organized, and it is important that the individual expectations and requirements of the participants are discussed.

Finally, project establishment supports the future management of the project. One of the major products of establishing the project formally is the project charter which — among other things — clarifies the assignment, the critical conditions, overall plans, and planned working practices. The project charter contains the project's most important contracts. A written formulation of the contracts contributes to focusing the project group's attention in case of future deviations and problematic situations.

It always pays to establish the project systematically

Establishment activities may be more or less extensive — but they always pay. The direct costs typically constitute two to five project group meetings, preparations for these meetings, and — where a few participants are concerned — preliminary analysis, design, and planning activities, and the writing of the project charter. The project group will also typically spend time on discussions and negotiations with other groups and individuals, and on training themselves. However, establishment costs merely reflect the characteristics of the individual projects, and they arise whether the project is systematically established or not. The direct costs are modest, and the potential advantages many. The thesis of this test is therefore that it always pays to establish the project systematically (thesis M4, Chapter 3).

It is important that the whole project group participates in the establishment activities. Most of the work can be done by a few participants, but all project group members must take part in the discussions and decisions which later will result in the project charter. This will give everyone the opportunity to influence the project, and the feeling of shared responsibility will increase. All project group members should thus participate in the two to five meetings during the establishment period, while only a few need to spend time on preparations and follow-up activities.

Topics

The following will give a more detailed description of the ingredients of project establishment. Some activities can take place within the setting

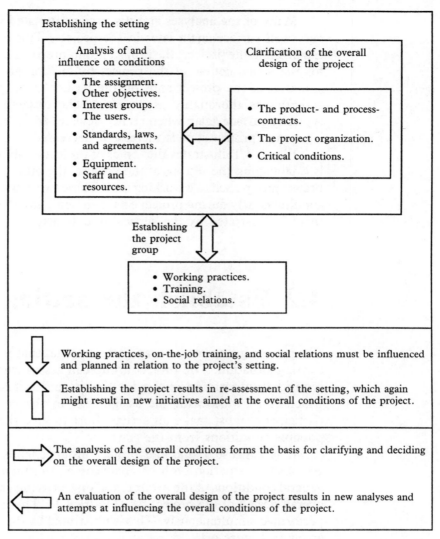

Figure 4.1 Topics of project establishment.

of the project, but many activities require that people from outside are enlisted. Whatever the circumstances, it is always important that major decisions and findings are in writing, and that they are approved by the involved parties. This will diminish the risk of misunderstandings and make it easier to detect deviations which may require intervention.

Many of the analyses and discussions initiated in this phase may very well surface again later in the project. This is only natural: by establishing the project, the project group prepares itself systematically for the actual course of the project by looking at the overall future situation of the project and, on the basis of this, planning the first activities as thoroughly as possible. The discussion will therefore typically surface again when reality deviates from what was expected, e.g. when project staff is increased, decreased or changed.

Figure 4.1 illustrates the topics of project establishment. One area is establishing the setting of the project, the other is establishing the project group itself as a working unit. These two activities are performed simultaneously during project establishment, and the relation between them is illustrated by the vertical double arrow.

4.2 Establish the setting

The project group must always keep in mind that it can influence the starting situation. The project group can assess what the assignment requires from a professional point of view, and as it is the project group which is to work with the assignment in the coming period, the participants must make an active effort to give the project the best possible conditions from the start.

It is suggested that the project group spends time during the establishment period both on analysing and influencing a number of general conditions of the project, and on clarifying and influencing the overall design of the project (see Figure 4.1). These two activities are performed simultaneously. This is illustrated by the horizontal double arrow in Figure 4.1.

It is not always clear from the outset what should be analysed and influenced. The important conditions of the project are often not known until later, when the plans are about to be realized, or when detailed design decisions are to be made. This means that the project group must anticipate that it will have to revise even fundamental conditions later in the project. A result of this revision may be that the project group must try to influence or change these conditions — and the design of the project.

Analysis of influence on conditions

The following will look at a number of general conditions which the project group may analyse and try to influence (see Figure 4.1).

Is the assignment formulated clearly?

The project must undertake a preliminary analysis of the assignment. What kind of product or service are they to deliver? What are the contractual relations? This analysis is very important, because the assignment and the contracts often make strict demands on the project design. If the assignment is not clearly defined, the user organization and its requirements must be thoroughly analysed during the project. If, on the other hand, the user organization has been able to formulate its requirements clearly and precisely, the project can move directly on to the design activities. Where the contracts are concerned, focus should be on the criteria for controlling and evaluating the project results. Figure 4.2 draws up a list of some of the relevant aspects to analyse in relation to the assignment.

What are the other objectives of the project?

The project may have other objectives than those closely linked to the assignment. Figure 4.3 gives some examples of such objectives. The project group must try to clarify these objectives and keep them

---

- Is the description of the assignment clear?

- Is the system to be used in relation to new working tasks, or is it to be used in relation to existing activities within the user organization?

- Is it a question of developing a new system, or a question of modifying an existing system?

- To what extent is hardware and systems software given?

- In what form are the contracts between the user organization, the development organization, and the project given?

- Who represents the other contractors?

- What are the possibilities and procedures for changing and re-negotiating the contracts?

- Which criteria and procedures are given for evaluation and control of the project's results?

- Which resources are at the project's disposal to handle the assignment?

- Is the division of responsibility in relation to the project clear?

Figure 4.2 Relevant aspects in relation to the assignment.

- Developing sub-products to be used in other projects.

- Improving the qualifications of the participants.

- Gaining experience in applying new techniques and tools.

- Giving the organization prestige.

- Giving the development organization experience in developing new types of applications.

Figure 4.3   Examples of other objectives.

in mind when assessing whether the given resources and conditions are realistic.

How will the interested parties influence the project?

An identification and analysis of the various parties interested in the project may help to clarify the mutual demands and needs for communication and negotiation during the course of the project. The project group must evaluate whether the project can be successfully performed on the basis of the existing agreements and contacts, or whether new agreements should be made and new — formal or informal — contacts established. Figure 4.4 gives some examples of prospective interested parties.

What part will the users play?

One of the decisive factors affecting the project and its results is the relation — or lack of relation — to the users.

In one project the project group had planned that the users were to participate in the design and test activities. Several times, however, the project group found that the users did not do as agreed. Later it turned out that the users had failed to understand why they had to participate actively, and what the project group expected of them. The users had not been involved in the planning of the cooperation.

In another case there was a tradition for each project to have one contact in the user organization. When this contact had sanctioned the user-oriented system description, the project group continued with their work without further help from the user organization. Time and time again, however, it turned out that the results were not acceptable to the users. Things had to be re-done or changed. The conclusion was that the communication lines during the project were far too narrow. Most people in the user organization had only vague ideas on what was going on in the project.

From a professional viewpoint the project group needs cooperation for several reasons:

- Which groups and individuals share an interest in the project?
- What is their interest, and how will they try to influence the project?
- Which interests do the project aim to satisfy?
- Who is affected by the project?
- Whom does the project group depend on?
- How will the project group act towards the various interested parties?

Interested parties outside the development organization:
- Users.
- The user organization.
- Unions.
- Suppliers.
- Clients.

Interested parties in the development organization:
- Parallel projects depending on the project.
- Management.
- Colleagues outside the project.
- The project group itself.
- Operation and maintenance.
- Sales and marketing.

Figure 4.4 Examples of interested parties.

- There is a need for the users' professional experience and competence. The project must exploit their knowledge about working tasks, organization, and traditions.

- There is a need for active cooperation in connection with tests, conversion, and training.

- Someone must be responsible for making decisions concerning the user organization.

- There is a need for the product to be accepted in the user organization.

At the same time still more users claim their right to participate actively in designing their own working situation. But how is this realized? How are the interests of the users represented? Figure 4.5 lists a number of different forms of user influence.

The project group's capability for cooperating with the user organization very much depends on the basic design of the project. If the project plays the role of supplier, the official communication lines are narrow. The system requirements are given. It is the task of the project to develop a computer system, and the user organization is responsible for training the users and for implementing the system. However, experience has shown that there is still a need for contact

- Participation in the project group.
- Participation in the reference group.
- Participation in the working group.
- Representation in the steering committee.
- Hearings.
- Negotiations.
- Formal agreements.

Possible participants—representatives of the following:
- Various user groups.
- Management of the user organization.
- Unions.

Figure 4.5   Possible forms of user influence.

and cooperation. In cases like that the project may be forced to establish informal contacts. If, on the other hand, the project plays the role of consultant in relation to the user organization, there is a better basis for establishing a productive cooperation. The project group must nevertheless keep in mind that the practical problems in getting the cooperation to work are almost always considerable. That is why user representatives must participate when the project is established.

The project group must identify and establish the necessary — formal and informal — agreements with and contacts to the users, management of the user organization, and the involved unions.

Is the project subjected to standards?

There are certain conditions which are difficult for the project group to influence. These include many of the standards, laws, and agreements the project has to obey. There may be many different conditions of this type, and it is the simple duty of the project group to know them and to consider them when the project is established. See Figure 4.6.

What equipment is available?

During the project the project group depends on having access to various types of equipment. In one project it turned out that the hardware and basic software for the new system could not be delivered as expected. When it was time for the programming work to begin, no equipment was available, and work in the project group came to a standstill. In another project the specifications of the basic software were suddenly changed with the result that a large part of the programming work had to be done all over again.

Figure 4.7 lists a number of relevant questions when considering available and desired equipment.

- Standards for designing projects. These standards will typically express the project and product policy of the development organization.

- Standards linked to the applied equipment.

- Standards linked to other related projects.

- Standards linked to the specific assignment.

- Laws and agreements regulating the design of the project.

- Laws and agreements regulating the design of the resulting system.

Figure 4.6 Various standards, laws, and agreements.

- What type of equipment does the project depend on?

- When and to what extent will the project need the equipment?

- Is the equipment tested and known to the project participants?

- Are there other projects which will use the same equipment?

- Is the equipment simultaneously used in operation?

- Who is responsible for the equipment?

Figure 4.7 Questions relating to the equipment.

Can the project get the necessary resources?

The most critical conditions of the project are manpower and other resources in the form of time, money, and capability of cooperation. The project group must estimate the assignment and assess the estimate in relation to the available resources. The project group must also clarify which resources it will need from the development organization and from the user organization.

The project group must estimate whether it has been staffed sufficiently, and whether the necessary experience and qualifications are present in the project. Another important thing to clarify is how the project is staffed over the total course of the project. In one development organization the tradition was to increase and decrease the staff in the course of the projects. People might suddenly be transferred to other — and supposedly — more important projects. The staff of the projects was often heavily increased just before a deadline.

Unstable allocation of manpower in a project usually proves ineffective because it takes time to re-establish project groups.

Clarification of the overall design of the project

Pay attention to the overall design of the project

So far the general conditions a project group must try to influence have been looked at. The objective of doing this is to create the best possible conditions for the project. At the same time, and as a consequence, the project group must influence and clarify the overall design of the project. See Figure 4.1.

First the product and process contracts must be made clear. A minimum requirement for what the contracts must contain is illustrated in Figure 4.8.

Secondly the organization of the project must be made clear (see Figure 4.9). Experience indicates that steering committees are seldom active, and that informal and personal contacts are more effective than

---

- The assignment.

- Other objectives.

- Criteria and procedures for evaluation of the project's results.

- Choice of equipment.

- Staff and other resources.

- Forms of cooperation and negotiation during the project.

- Time limits.

Figure 4.8   Minimum requirements for contents of project contracts.

- The structure of the project organization. Are there a steering committee and reference groups?

- Division of responsibility and competence between groups.

- Frequency of meetings and management of the groups.

- Information between groups.

Figure 4.9   Minimum requirements for description of the project organization.

reference groups. If the project group wants support from the organization, the system developers must actively influence the way the project is organized. In situations where the conditions of the project start slipping a strong steering committee, with competence from both the development and the user organization, can prove valuable. The project group is clearly interested in influencing and cultivating the project organization, so that it holds a strong position in the development process.

Thirdly, the critical prerequisites of the project must be made clear. The contractual conditions of the project organization in themselves constitute the overall design of the project - but what are the assumptions and choices behind this design?

The project groups' alertness to future deviations and critical situations will increase considerably if the critical prerequisites — manpower, time, forms of cooperation, equipment, etc. — are made clear from the beginning. This will also serve the project group in case of future disagreements or conflicts between the project group and the surrounding environment. It is just as important to clarify the critical prerequisites as it is to clarify the overall design of the project itself.

4.3 Establish the project group

Establish a professionally and socially well-functioning working unit

Now we will turn to the other objective of establishing the project: to get the project group to work as a professionally and socially well-functioning unit. See Figure 4.1. A good setting does not do it alone. A poor setting may obstruct a successful project, but a good setting cannot ensure it.

In many cases the discussions and decisions made at a project group meeting are not taken seriously. Decisions may not even be taken down in writing, and they may not be followed up. The shared feeling of responsibility is not very high. And maybe the allocation of tasks in the project is not supported by the possibility of speaking openly about the problems connected with the individual tasks. Status may not be reported systematically, making it difficult for the individual project

Project establishment. Project establishment includes sharing experiences, planning of training before and during the project, and an initial analysis of the assignment.

member to obtain a comprehensive understanding of the project. The result is that the individual project member concentrates on his or her own task without thinking of the project as a whole.

In one project many of the detailed decisions linked to the design of the new system were of a more or less random nature. It turned out that even though all the project members knew the assignment, most of them had failed to understand the fundamental ideas. The detailed design activities were based on the original description of the assignment, and the project group had not spent any time on trying to understand the problems and objectives behind the assignment.

Establishing the project formally embraces — as already mentioned

— most of the aspects of the system development project. The project group must plan its working practices, and this requires that part of the analysis, design, and planning work is done at this stage. Decision should be made whether the project should be based on experimental working practices or on classical analysis followed by design and implementation activities. The first overall plan must be worked out, and techniques and tools for solving the various assignments must be chosen. These fundamental elements in planning the project group's working practices will not be discussed further here. Other chapters in this book contain advice and guidelines on these important issues.

Here cooperation in the project group will be discussed, along with management of the project, training, and socialization. These are all subjects which belong under the heading of project establishment.

Cooperation in the group

Groups consist of individuals. The objective is to exploit the differences between these individuals. The experience and competence of each participant must be utilized, and a basis for professional and personal development created. It is also important, however, that the group functions as one unit, and that the individual participant feels common responsibility.

The expectations and demands of each participant must be formulated as clearly as possible when the project is being established so that they can form the basis of the future work. If they are not discussed at this stage, they might surface later in the form of disguised conflicts and power struggles. One of the meetings during project establishment should discuss what each participant requires or expects of the project as regards professional improvement, further training, future career, and personal development. There are obviously limits to how detailed and personal a discussion like that can get, but the project group will always benefit from discussing these issues as seriously and openly as possible.

The project group must also discuss attitudes to some basic group processes. The group may, for instance, discuss the questions listed in Figure 4.10 and together try to decide how these processes could be enacted in the group.

1. What kind of working practices should be applied when the project group generates ideas?

2. What kind of working practices should be applied when the project group works with different suggestions?

3. How are decisions made in the project group? (Does the project leader make all decisions alone — must there be total agreement, or is there right of veto?)

4. How does the project group help the individual to maintain good relations to the organization they originally refer to?

5. How does the project group introduce working practices which are just as open with respect to interaction in the group as with respect to the project's more technical assignments?

6. What kind of behaviour results in success and failure, respectively?

7. How can the project group ensure working norms which make fighting for the good ideas of others just as natural as fighting for one's own?

8. What should the project group do in case of strong personal disagreements — maybe even conflict?

Figure 4.10   Questions in relation to some basic group processes.

- Relation to management of the development organization.

- Relation to the rest of the development organization.

- Planning and evaluation.

- Planning project group meetings.

- Acting as chairman on meetings.

- Taking down minutes on meetings.

- Allocating assignments.

- Quality assurance.

- Configuration management.

Figure 4.11   Management tasks to be distributed.

Management of projects

*Who is
responsible for
performing
management
activities?*

Why should only one person — the project leader — be responsible for all, or even most, management activities? If everyone participates in the planning, evaluation, and regulation activities, attention to management problems will increase. The whole group will be alert should unexpected and critical situations arise. Most people will also find it more professionally satisfying to participate in the management activities in their own projects. A shared feeling of responsibility in the project group, however, requires commitment and knowledge.

Traditions and requirements from the project's environment will often be decisive for how management tasks can be distributed. The project group should in any case always discuss the possibilities and problems before management tasks are distributed. Some of the important management tasks are listed in Figure 4.11.

In some projects only very few prepare for the project group meetings, and the meetings are conducted in a loose and unstructured way. In other projects the meetings are conducted very rigidly according to a standard agenda, where many project group members may find it hard to come forward with their problems and opinions. The project group meeting is an important opportunity to exchange information, to establish an open attitude and a shared feeling of responsibility, and to discuss the problems and conflicts surfacing during the project. Hence the project group must pay special attention to preparing these meetings. Figure 4.12 could be a starting point.

Training

The project group must make up its mind about its need for training before, during, and after the project. What experience and what competence is represented in the project group? What is required to handle the assignment? Do the planned working practices or the applied equipment call for special requirements? If further qualifications are required, the form of training must be discussed: study groups, enlisting of external people, participation in external courses, etc.

Socialization

Most of the issues mentioned above affect the social relations in the group. Experience indicates that establishing the project thoroughly

- How is the agenda worked out?

- What are the standard items on the agenda?

- What should be discussed on the meetings? What should not?

- How can a satisfactory degree of preparation be ensured?

- How much should be taken down in writing on the meetings?

- Should the meetings be evaluated? How often should the course of the project be taken up for evaluation?

- How are the tasks allocated in relation to the project group meetings?

- How often should the project group meet?

Figure 4.12   Preparing project group meetings.

strengthens the project professionally as well as socially. Experience also indicates that it often proves fruitful to discuss social — and even personal — issues. However, social relations are not formed through discussions alone — they are formed during the process itself. It is therefore good to consider both the process and the social relations in preparing to establish a project. Maybe it would be a good idea to incorporate a two-day seminar away from your place of work?

4.4 The project charter

The project charter must stipulate the important decisions

An important product resulting from establishing the project is the project charter. A minimum requirement for the project charter is that it contains the most important decisions concerning the overall design and working practices of the project. As an ideal the project charter should reflect the conclusions and consequences of the many analyses and discussions which took place during project establishment. Apart from that, however, very little can be said about how extensive and detailed the project charter should be. Figure 4.13 gives an example of a possible list of contents.

The project charter should, however, include a summary of the

---

CONTENTS

1. **Setting**

   1.1 Objectives
   1.2 Resources
        1.2.1 Staff
        1.2.2 Tools
   1.3 Organization in relation to other projects
   1.4 Organization in relation to the company's basic organization

2. **Working practices in the project**

   2.1 Choice of project model
   2.2 The project group
   2.3 Technical coordination group
   2.4 Other working groups
        2.4.1 Principles of allocating staff
        2.4.2 Competence
   2.5 Planning
   2.6 Project meetings
   2.7 Seminars
   2.8 Decision making

3. **Critical prerequisites**

Figure 4.13   An example of a list of contents for a project charter.

contracts the project is subject to. To avoid future misunderstandings, the written contracts concerning groups or people outside the project group should be presented to and approved by these groups or people. The project charter should also contain an initial version of the plan and of the product design, and it should contain a reference to more detailed documents. It would be useful to let the project charter be an internal document in the project group, and let the contracts with other parties be special documents.

With an interval of a couple of months the actual course of the project should be compared with the project charter. Such an evaluation may lead to modifications of the project and changes in the project's setting.

It hardly pays to keep the project charter up to date as one coherent document. However, the project charter must naturally be updated and changed throughout the project. This will partly take place as old plans are changed, or new plans discussed. Another good idea is to keep a check on the changes in the charter by adding new pages to the original project charter.

Exercise 4.1

Plan the establishment of a project

Make a plan for establishing a project. Choose one of the projects you have participated in, or choose one you are about to participate in.

- In what setting should the establishment activities take place?

- Which establishment activities should be performed?

- What should the agenda for these activities look like?

- In what order would you suggest that the items are discussed?

- How many resources would the activity require?

4.5 Obstacles increase the need

In reality it is not always that easy

It pays to establish the project systematically. This chapter has already argued in favour of this. A number of ideas have also been presented for what this activity should contain, and how it could be carried out. In practice, however, it often proves difficult to establish the project systematically. Figure 4.14 summarizes a number of typical obstacles. Paradoxically these obstacles often reflect the fact that the project's setting is unclear, and this gives all the more reason for establishing the project systematically.

The project is staffed gradually

Project group members are often affiliated to the new project as they get disengaged from their old ones. There may be a plan which decides

- The project is staffed gradually.

- It is unclear when the project will start.

- The project group is hard to delimit.

- There is a lack of commitment.

- The activity is swallowed up by competing activities.

- The project leader is in any case solely responsible.

Figure 4.14   Obstacles to systematic project establishment.

when each member is to start on the new project, but the plan rarely holds. Practice often proves it difficult to find an appropriate date for establishing the project. And every time new colleagues are attached to the project, the group has to spend time and energy on introducing them into the environment which was created during project establishment.

The project group can try to get a list of the people who are to participate in the project, and an indication of when they will start. This will facilitate enlising future participants in the project establishment activities. However, this is not an ideal solution as their minds will probably still be on their current projects. Another possibility is to let new project members work with activities that do not require extensive introductions to the project. Later, at some appropriate time, the new group should then be established more systematically. Furthermore the project charter should be worked out so that it can be applied as an introduction for new project members.

It is unclear when the project will start

When does a project really start? Is it before or after the feasibility study? Is it before or after the contracts have been signed? How much do you need to know about the project before it pays to establish it systematically?

There are no precise answers to these questions. Experience indicates that project establishment should not be prolonged. If there are important gaps in the group's knowledge about the project at the time the project is established, project activities might be defined to fill these gaps. Furthermore, it might, as already indicated, be planned to re-establish the project at some later stage.

The project group is hard to delimit

Who should participate when the project is established? What is a project group? The borderline between system developers and users is not always very clear. The user organization may have its own computer specialists who collaborate with the staff from the development organization, or the user organization might be responsible for developing parts of the system.

It is important to clarify who is responsible for what in the project, and what the mutual expectations are — but it can be unmanageable and alarming to enlist too many people in the project establishment activities. One possibility is to start in a group which has a natural common interest, and then enlist other people in specific activities that concern them.

Lack of commitment

There will often be people in the project who are not very committed to the project, and who have no interest in trying to influence it. They may be more deeply engaged in another project, or they may not be very ambitious. Ideally everyone in the project group should feel responsible. And certainly, project establishment ensures a higher degree of commitment, even though the activity cannot ensure that everybody will feel that way. In any case project establishment presents an opportunity of influencing people's commitment, or to clarify that all participants do not share the same degree of commitment.

The activity is swallowed up by competing activities

It may prove difficult to get the whole group together to establish the project. The various members are typically engaged in the maintenance of newly implemented systems. Such activities are hard to plan since they typically arise as errors which should be corrected as quickly as possible — preferably at once. Establishing the project is an activity with a long-term effect, and it is all too easy — in a tight situation — to argue that it would not make any difference to postpone a couple of meetings. That is why it would be a good idea to arrange a seminar away from the workplace.

The project leader is in any case solely responsible

It is all very good to distribute management tasks. But often one person is appointed to take sole responsibility if things go wrong. A prerequisite of distributing responsibility in the group is the acceptance and support of management. Otherwise it will be necessary for the project leader to know all the aspects of the project anyway, and others will typically leave the whole responsibility to the projects leader if things get problematic.

All the more reason

Project establishment can easily come to nothing if the project group is facing some of the obstacles described above. These obstacles may make it difficult to see how to get started in a more systematic manner.

Exercise 4.2

Plan a re-establishment seminar

Make a plan for a re-establishment seminar in your project. The reason for the seminar could be that new participants are to be introduced into the project, or that the project group needs to evaluate the status of the project. Maybe the project has been established already, but now a well-defined situation has been reached (a baseline — see Chapter 7), and the participants finally work together as a group.

What makes this situation different from planning the establishment of a project group (see Exercise 4.1)?

A project group about to establish a project needs advice about, and guidelines for, how this can be done in their own development organization. Local traditions must be established and experience must be gained. This will take time, but it is important. Experience may be disseminated in the form of concrete advice and guidelines as a supplement to this chapter.

Further reading

The authors have not encountered any literature on project establishment as a subject in its own right. However, project establishment is often dealt with on courses and seminars under the heading 'project start-up'. The questions in Figure 4.10 concerning some basic group processes are listed according to Schönfeldt (1983). The main elements of this chapter are based on experience from the MARS project, see, e.g. MARS 9 (1985).

5 Planning — the key to success

The plan should encourage commitment

*System
developers
design two
things: the
product and the
process*

System developers are creative people. They love to design a system, and they spend a lot of time discussing different design proposals. Sometimes they forget that they design two things. Namely the computer-based system, as well as the working process which is to result in that system. Everyone obviously makes a plan for this working process. If for no other reason than because the surrounding world expects it. But the plan is often ascribed very little importance. This may be because many people find that it is based on unrealistic expectations to deadlines and product quality.

It pays to be diligent when the plan is made. The project plan is a contract between the project group and its environment and as such it should commit all involved parties. However, this requires that everyone believes that it is possible to follow the plan — the plan must therefore be convincing. Ideally the plan should serve as a common reference basis during discussions about the project and when project tasks are given priority.

Planning is part of the 15 to 25 per cent of the project work which is process-oriented (management). The process-oriented activities ensure that the effort, through which the concrete results of the project are created, is employed in a reasonable manner. Planning is the basis for regulating the working practices and evaluating the project status — and, in some cases, for revising the plans. Thorough planning is one important key to success.

This chapter gives some advice and guidelines concerning project planning. The focus is on the project plan, i.e. the overall plan of the project. Section 5.1 discusses what planning is, and how it is linked to evaluation and regulation of the project. Section 5.2 stresses the importance of written plans, and formulates some requirements concerning the functionality of the project plan. Section 5.3 contains a proposal for a minimum standard for a project plan. Section 5.4 gives some advice and guidelines concerning the form of the project plan, and also gives some advice which may come in useful if you get stuck. Sections 5.5 and 5.6 present some techniques which may be employed in connection with project planning, estimating resources, and analysing activity networks. They are techniques for evaluation of the quantitative elements in the project plan. Section 5.7 discusses the application of computer-based planning tools. It is recommended that these are employed in large projects because this promotes written plans, among other reasons. Computer-based tools do not, however, ensure an acceptable quality of the plans.

5.1 Planning should facilitate evaluation and regulation

System developers are often in the enviable situation that they are given the chance of designing their own working process. Planning is designing a project where the most important element is a working process. System developers often have very few restrictions when they organize their working practices. The conditions of system development projects, however, make planning a difficult task: the deadlines and the available resources are often determined from the beginning and are not expected to be changed, even though the objective of the project is unclear.

A system development project's costs are very high. Hence it is necessary throughout the project to relate the actual progress and costs to expectations. The expectations are expressed in the plans. The plans facilitate evaluation and regulation of the project. Planning, evaluation, and regulation together constitute the process-oriented part of systems development, i.e. those activities which are called management. Table 5.1 gives an outline of the connection between management functions

Function	Intended results	Intended relations to project contracts
Evaluation	• Understanding working practices and conditions. • Evaluation of distance between plans and status. • Identification of errors, problems, and conflicts.	• Forms the basis of design and revision of process contracts • Evaluation of process contracts.
Planning	• Plans on different levels. • Description of conditions required by the plans.	• Based on product contracts • Results in process contracts. • Consists of refinement and clarification of process contracts.
Regulation	• Changed working practices. • Changed qualifications, attitudes, and expectations of participants. • Changed conditions in the project, including changed contracts.	• Subject to process contracts. • May result in re-negotiation of process contract. • Affects internal contracts

Table 5.1 The connection between management functions on the one hand and intended results and relations to project contracts on the other (Figure 3.10).

on the one hand, and the intended results and relations to project contracts on the other hand.

System development projects are characterized by a high degree of uncertainty. Unexpected and problematic situations arise during the course of the project. Effective management thus requires a current and thorough insight into the course of the project. A system development project must therefore be organized in a way which ensures direct and close interaction between performance and management activities.

Planning should result in plans on different levels. Partly an overall plan, the project plan, and partly more detailed plans on subgroup and individual levels. These plans may be seen as process contracts between the involved parties. This chapter will primarily discuss planning on project level.

Active collective planning

Only project participants know enough to make realistic plans

As many of the project participants as possible should actively participate in planning. This will ensure a higher degree of commitment to the plan, and this is a prerequisite of making realistic plans. One principle is that it is important that all the involved parties understand and accept the plan (principle M8, Chapter 3).

Active collective planning improves the quality of the plans. System development projects are characterized by uncertain objectives and changing conditions, and the project participants are closest to clarifying the objectives. Another principle is that project participants are the only ones who know enough to make realistic plans (principle M7, Chapter 3).

By actively planning the project together, the participants also ensure effective regulation of the process because communication about plans is improved. The shared feeling of responsibility for the plans must not, however, lead to a situation where no-one feels personally responsible for taking management initiatives. The principle here is that it is necessary to plan with management activities, and that these activities constitute 15 to 25 per cent of the work in the project (principle M10, Chapter 3).

Planning requires compromises

Planning is a question of creating a balance. Every project is a compromise between costs, duration, and quality (see Figure 5.1). The project group often finds itself in the unsatisfactory situation that it can only regulate on product quality. Costs and duration are determined by others. In situations like that it may become necessary to try to influence the fundamental conditions of the project. The desired balance should, however, in any case be formulated in the project plan. From then on the project group is responsible for doing what it can to follow the plan, and if this turns out to be impossible, to draw attention to the fact that the project is getting out of balance.

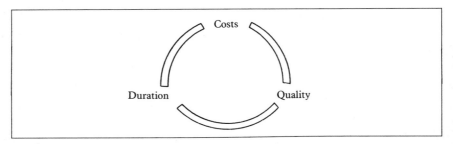

Figure 5.1   Factors which should be in balance.

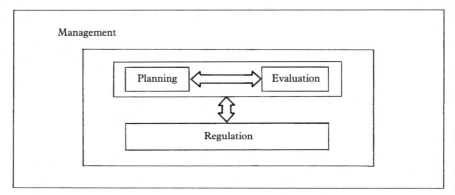

Figure 5.2   The process-oriented parts of system development.

Interaction between management activities

Management activities should be performed concurrently

The mutual interaction between management activities is illustrated in Figure 5.2 and elaborated on in Chapter 3.

Evaluation and planning are mutually dependent and should therefore be performed concurrently (principle M1, Chapter 3). Planning takes its starting point in an evaluation of the situation. Plans are useless if they presuppose resources which turn out to be unavailable or unsuitable. Surprises cannot be avoided, but the evaluation activity should attempt to expose the uncertainties and thus further need for planning. The plan is the basis for evaluating the distance between status and expectations. These evaluations give an impression of what progress the project is making, and they might reveal a need for a more thorough evaluation of the situation as well as a revision of the plans.

Process-oriented reflection (planning and evaluation) and regulation of the process affect each other, and should therefore be performed concurrently (principle M2, Chapter 3). New plans form the basis for regulating the working process. Implementing a plan is the same as regulating the project. Examples are a changed division of labour, a changed level of ambition, or employing a new colleague. Regulation ensures, on the other hand, an improved understanding of the project and its conditions. Regulation may therefore disclose a need for renewed evaluation and perhaps revision of the plan.

Planning is to find a way

Planning can be compared with finding the way between two locations in a landscape. Usually you have a map (= a description of the conditions of the project). You choose and draw in the route you wish to follow (= the plan). The route may be divided into stages, each of which is defined by a start and a terminal point (= intermediate products). Maybe the stages must be completed at a certain point in time. To be able to find your way, you must be able to determine where you are on the map (= master project evaluation techniques). Most of all you must be able to determine whether you have reached the terminal points (= evaluate whether the intermediate products meet the specified quality requirements). You may be confronted with deviations: either you lose your way, or you find that the route you had planned to follow is closed. Or you might decide to go somewhere else. In case of deviations like that you have to draw in a new route on the map (= revise the plan).

System development projects can often be compared to expeditions into unknown territories. No one has been there before, there are no maps, and — even worse — the destination of the expedition is not really known. The explorers who accomplished and survived the expeditions might have been lucky, but they were also good planners, evaluators, and regulators. Of course, only part of the work in systems development can be compared to expeditions. Coding input or print programs is often a routine task. Testing may also develop into a routine task. Projects consisting of adding report facilities to existing systems are often routine tasks. Thorough planning is not all that necessary for the quality and efficiency of the work in situations like that. Routine tasks should obviously be included in the overall plans, but they need not be planned in detail.

5.2 The plan should be in writing

The over-riding principle is that the project plan should facilitate evaluation. That is why the plan should always be in writing and should contain evaluation criteria and procedures (principle M6, Chapter 3). The written project plan supports several functions. The plan is an indispensable aid in the more detailed planning of the project. The plan also plays an important role in the project's internal and external communication.

The project plan is a model of the course of the project. The plan should describe how the different parts of the project will develop in time, and how these parts can remain in balance. Manpower resources, organization, and time should, for instance, balance with expectations of activities, which again should balance with expectations of services and products. The plan should document the expectations of the project so that it is possible to check that the expectations are in balance, that they are realistic, and that they are actually fulfilled. The plan should include quantitative expectations of resources and duration, and qualitative expectations of services and products, of the participants' qualifications, and of the interaction between activities, resources, and products.

The project plan should make the following processes possible:

- Evaluation of whether the different expectations to the project are in balance, and whether the plan is realisic.

- Evaluation of the distance between the actual and the expected state of the project.

- Evaluation of the consequences of changing the project's conditions.

- Planning sub-projects or single activities in more detail.

- Regulation by sub-groups or individuals of their own working practices so that these contribute to the expected course of the project. The people involved should be able 'to see themselves' in the plan.

- Planning by the project's environmental contacts of their own working practices on the basis of their interests in, and their interfaces with the project.

Figure 5.3   Requirements of the project plan's functionality.

*Oral
descriptions
conceal
weaknesses
better than
written ones*

A good plan makes it possible for the various participants in the project to see how the individual activities contribute to the project's overall progress. A good plan also increases the transparency of the process. The plan acts as a 'whip' and 'carrot' by making it possible to see the project's progress or lack of progress.

Figure 5.3 lists the most important functional attributes of a project plan. These attributes can only be satisfied in a written plan. It is all too easy to bypass unpleasant weaknesses if the plan is only formulated orally.

No plan.

5.3 Minimum standard for project plan

*A minimum
standard should
be supplemented
with advice
and guidelines*

A minimum standard expresses the requirements a specific type of product must always meet. A minimum standard may be locally supplemented in the development organization or in the project with a more detailed standard adapted to the local conditions. The minimum requirements may furthermore be supplemented with advice and guidelines concerning planning activities, for instance in the form of checklists. We have drawn up the minimum standard of the project plan's contents on the basis of the functionality requirements formulated in the previous chapter. The next section will describe some of the advice and guidelines concerning project planning which supplement the minimum requirements.

The minimum standard is presented in Figure 5.4. The first requirement is that the plan should contain an account of all the project's main components. The second requirement is that the interaction between the components is described, and that the balance between the components is documented, i.e. it should be argued that the activities can be performed with the available resources in the available organization, and that the activities will result in the stated products, services, and side-effects. The third requirement is that the plan accounts for the consequences of changed conditions and resources.

The project plan must contain descriptions of:

1. **The project's main components**

   • Resources.
   • Conditions.
   • Organization.
   • Activities.
   • Products and services.
   • Side-effects.

   There must be a description of the time when each resource, condition, form of organization, etc. occurs. Intermediate products must be grouped into baselines.

   The level of detail depends on the project situation (routine, problem-solving, problem-setting) and the temporal distance to the phenomenon (impending activities should be described in more detail than later activities). On the whole the descriptions should be reasonably unambiguous for the involved parties.

2. **Relations in the project plan**

   The project plan must argue

   • That the activities can be carried out with the available resources under the given conditions on the basis of the available intermediate products.
   • That the activities will result in the desired products and services, and that they only give the desired side-effects.
   • That the activity schedule is consistent.

3. **Critical conditions**

   Obvious risks must be discussed. What could go wrong, what are the consequences, and — if something goes wrong — what can be done?

Figure 5.4   Minimum standard for content of the project plan.

Division of project work

The standard in Figure 5.4 requires that intermediate products are organized in baselines (see Chapter 7). A baseline is a coordinated project state to which everyone participating in the project can refer. When a project has reached a baseline, intermediate products are in well-defined states, and other important prerequisites are known. The description of a baseline should include criteria and procedures for how it can be ascertained that a baseline has been reached.

Checkpoints are those points in time where it is planned to check whether a baseline has been reached. Planning with baselines and checkpoints makes it possible to determine whether the project runs according to plan. If a checkpoint reveals that the described baseline has not been reached, you either plan new activities and a new checkpoint a little later in the project, or you define a new baseline corresponding to the actual state of the intermediate products, and then change the plans accordingly.

Baselines and checkpoints are superior to phases

A phase is defined as the set of activities performed between two checkpoints. Traditionally a phase is defined by describing its main activities (see example in Figure 5.5). Intermediate products are rarely defined, and they are not grouped into baselines. The traditional phase description is an insufficient basis for efficiently evaluating the state of the project. It is far more easy and more operational to ascertain whether the project has reached a described baseline than it is to ascertain a qualitatively satisfactory conclusion of some activities. The traditional phase plan illustrated in Figure 5.5 does not include any checkpoints offering the possibility of an overall assessment of the project's progress. The specification phase should result in a system specification, but the construction phase has been initiated and is halfway concluded before the specification phase is terminated. How would it be possible — at this point in time — to evaluate whether there is a need for changing the plan or regulating the working practices? Our principle is that baselines and checkpoints are superior to phases. Obviously you still need to divide the project into phases. However, phases are unsuitable as a fundamental means to divide the work in the project, because phases confuse time and content. Thus they impede dynamic regulation of the course of the project (principle M5, Chapter 3).

Experience indicates that qualitative weaknesses in the initial analysis and design activities often pass unrecognized until they turn into problems during programming, test, and conversion. A project running according to a traditional phase plan usually observes the time

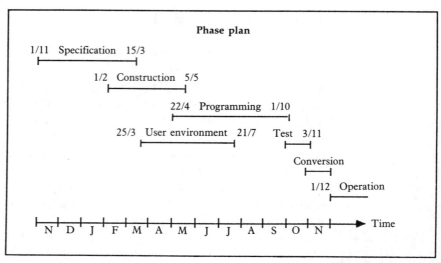

Figure 5.5   An example of a traditional phase plan which confuses time and content, thus constituting a poor basis for evaluating the state of the project.

schedule in the initial phases, but the project often gets stuck and fails to follow the plans during the programming and test phases. It might turn out that the quality of the overall design is not good enough, or that the plan does not take into account that there might be a need for new analysis and design activities.

There is a need for distinguishing between at least two dimensions of the work in the project. On the one hand there is a need for a temporal distinction for managing the progress of the project. On the other hand there is a need for a material distinction between work requiring different working practices.

Traditional phases confuses time and content

The traditional division of project work into phases confuses temporal and material dimensions, and fails to account for the mutual interaction between different types of work. A phase is traditionally a limited space of time which delimits a specific type of work. The phase plan in Figure 5.5 fails to account for the fact there there will in all probability be a need for construction and programming work during the test phase. 'Well, then we will just have to resume the construction and programming phases' might be a rection to that argument. However, this contradicts the idea of using the phases as a temporal separation of the project work. A conceptual distinction between a temporal and a material division of the work is very useful. Temporally a project may

---

Temporal division — which checkpoints?

- When is there a need for evaluating the situation in the project seen in relation to the development organization or user organization?

- How often does the project group need to undertake an overall evaluation of the situation in the project?

- What products and services should result from the individual phases?

Material division — which activities?

- What should constitute checkable baselines?

- Which activities should be undertaken to produce the desired products and services?

- Which criteria and procedures should be defined for evaluation of products and services?

Figure 5.6   Planning the temporal and material division of the project work.

be divided into phases with checkpoints, and materially a product may be divided into activities. Figure 5.6 lists a number of relevant questions in this connection.

Example of a plan

The following will present an outline of a plan for a project developing an application system.

1. Assignment   Developing a computer-based system supporting bank employees in the local branches in serving customers within the field of bank loans.

2. Conditions   The first version of the application system is expected to be put into production 18 months after project start. This version must live up to the overall functional requirements described in the project charter. A new terminal system is currently being implemented in the user organization. The user organization and the development organization have great expectations of this project, because it is the first banking application which is to be developed for the new equipment. The considerable costs for the equipment are expected to be balanced by computer-supported improvements in the bank's customer service.

3. Resources   *People.* The project group is staffed with five system developers all through the project. Two of these people are user consultants. They have knowledge of the user organization and of equivalent systems. They have 3 to 5 years' experience with training of users, documentation for users, and analysis and design of computer systems on a functional level. The remaining three people are planners and programmers with different experiences. One has worked as a programmer for five years, two of which were spent in this development organization developing on-line systems. Another has just finished his programmer education and has just been employed by this development organization. The third person has eight years of experience in this development organization developing batch programs and is responsible for maintaining parts of these programs. None of the project participants have any project management experience.

Equipment. Terminal system and central system, as well as system development systems, including tools for prototyping.

4. Products and services

The project should deliver the following products and services:

- First version of the computer system as described in the project charter.
- Maintenance documentation.
- User manual.
- User training.
- Conversion.

5. Side-effects

Furthermore the following side-effects are required:

- Training a new employee.
- Experience in developing banking systems with distributed data bases.

6. Organization

The project organization consists of a steering committee and a project group, as well as two working groups in two pilot branches of the user organization.

7. Baselines

Baseline 1. Description of current banking practices is concluded and visions of computer applications are described in the form of a prototype of a display screen dialogue and a description of innovations in the banking practices.

Baseline 2. Overall design is concluded.

Baseline 3. On-line part and batch part ready for test of interfaces.

Baseline 4. Version 1 ready for user test.

Baseline 5. Version 1 ready for conversion and production.

Baseline 6. Version 1 converted and evaluated after three months in production.

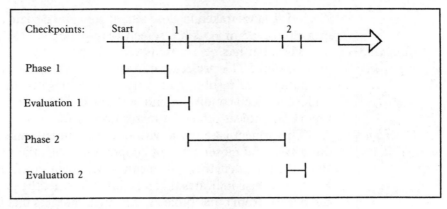

Figure 5.7.

**8. Time
schedule
(extract)**

(See Figure 5.7.)

**9. Survey of
activities
(extract)**

Phase 1:

- Formal project establishment.
- Analysis of existing computer systems.
- Analysis of bank work.
- Generating ideas and building up visions.
- Design and programming of prototypes.
- Evaluation of prototypes.
- Analysis of technical possibilities for interaction with other systems.
- Detailed planning of phase 2.

Phase 2.

- Start-up phase 2.
- . . . .

**10. Description
of activities
(extract)**

Phase 1.
. . . *Analysis of banking activities:* Analysis is undertaken in cooperation between the project group and the working groups in two pilot branches of the bank. For the first two months the groups meet every other week for a two-day session. The project group applies Newman's techniques for description of office work, and some of DeMarco's techniques for description of computer-based systems. Ideas for computer applications generated during the analysis activities are written down in diaries.

Analysis is undertaken in close interaction with design and programming of a prototype of possible screen play dialogues.

11. Correlations in the project plan

The plan has been discussed and approved in the whole project organization. The project group expects that the activities will lead to the anticipated results, and that the activities can be carried through under the given conditions and with the available resources. A separate report on project effort estimates argues for this.

12. Problematic prerequisites

The project is to work with new equipment, and it is going to try out a new and closer form of cooperation with the user organization. It is unclear what this will mean to the project effort and schedule. Experience also indicates that it is difficult to get the project participants disengaged from other projects. The plan requires that everybody works full time in the project from the beginning. If this is not the case baseline 1, and to a greater extent baseline 2, will not be reached at the planned checkpoints.

Exercise 5.1

Evaluate some project plans

Find some concrete examples of project plans and assess their applicability as a basis for evaluating and regulating the course of the project.

Assess the plans on the basis of the minimum standard in Figure 5.4 and on the basis of the assertion that baselines and checkpoints are better than traditional phases. Take Chapter 7 into the discussion.

5.4 Project planning: advice and guidelines

We distinguish between three types of project situations: routine, problem-solving, and problem-setting situations (see Chapter 2). In routine situations the problem or task is well known, as are the procedures for handling the task. The task is also known in problem-solving situations, but there is uncertainty or lack of knowledge about what procedure to apply. In problem-setting situations the situation itself is unclear to the participants. Something must be done, but no one is certain what the problem or the task is — and thus no one knows what the procedure should be. All planning is not the same. Some planning tasks are a matter of routine. Most of them are problem-solving tasks, but sometimes the planning activity turns into a situation which resembles problem setting. The project assignment is normally determined in the project establishment activities, but conditions might have changed later on. In that case one could ask the following questions:

- What are the most important project objectives? Which groups are interested in these objectives?

- What is difficult in the project? Where is it likely that errors, problems, and conflicts will arise?

Attempts at answering these questions may lead to activities which we normally do not call planning activities, but which nevertheless are important to carry out before we return to the classical problem-solving activities in the planning process.

Planning is normally problem solving

Planning is normally a problem-solving activity. It is a question of making the pieces of a jigsaw puzzle fit. Some of the pieces are given beforehand by virtue of contracts concerning the product, conditions in the development organization, available resources, etc. Other pieces are optional, for instance working practices and internal organization. Some pieces will turn out to be missing — the project plan is deficient. This may be caused by lack of resources, inexpedient division into versions, lack of knowledge concerning the interface to other projects, or too high ambitions. In situations like this planning should turn into an evaluation activity, which might have to be tackled quite differently. Figure 5.8 gives some advice on and guidelines for project planning which may prove useful if the project is stuck, or if it is difficult to get started.

It is recommended that the individual development organization collects experience from project planning in its own set of advice and guidelines. On a more general level some advice and guidelines, linked to the minimum standard of the project plan, are as follows:

Problem solving. Problem-solving situations require that the system developers master different working practices which they can try to apply to the problem.

- One of the conditions of the project is the project's dependency on other projects. This is an important but often overlooked condition of the plan's implementability. Many problems in systems development are connected to the high degree of parallel development usually taking place. Applications are often developed concurrently

---

- Make an outline of the project plan on the basis of the minimum standard in Section 5.3.

- Ask yourselves the question: What would we like to know about the work we are about to start? What is unclear?

- Classify all the known information about the main components of the project and write them down under the relevant headings.

- Go carefully into each section and try to make it complete.

- Make sure that the project plan is coherent.

- Consider the elements of risk.

- If you should get stuck, go on to some other section.

- Think of some other project. What was done there?

- Good ideas require some time to ripen. Take a break once in a while.

Figure 5.8 Advice and guidelines: project planning.

with development, adaptation, or installation of hardware and basic software.

- It is important to consider and document the connection between the project's main components. It is, for instance, important that the people assigned to carry out the activities in the project have the proper qualifications. If the necessary qualifications are not present in the project, training activities should be included in the plans.

- It is important to consider the elements of risk and account for the consequences for the project in case of changed conditions and resources. Naturally it is impossible to anticipate all conceivable changes, but the more consequences the plan describes, the easier it is to see and prevent serious changes in the project.

Plan with planning
- An out-dated plan is useless. The plan should be kept up to date. The idea of written plans is not to file non-current plans away, and have the actual plan inside your head — the transparency would be gone then. Therefore time should be set aside from the beginning to allow for revision and refinement of the plans. It should also be determined when new versions of the plan are available.

Figure 5.9 gives some advice and guidelines concerning the form of the project plan.

The project plan should be described in short and precise terms. The plan is a working document, not a novel or a textbook.

The project should be described in identifiable terms:
- Where people are concerned qualifications (education and experience) and availability should be indicated.
- Where computer tools are concerned attributes and availability should be indicated.
- Under project organization it should be described who is responsible for each activity, and the form of communication in the project (meetings, memos, etc.).
- Activities and services should be described by commonly known names and applied methods, techniques, and working practices.
- Products and intermediate products should be described by attributes later to be tested or evaluated.

Time and extent should be indicated if at all possible.

Refer to existing documents: the project charter, contracts, design documents.

Employ diagrams.

Employ word processing so that the plan is easy to revise.

Figure 5.9 Advice and guidelines: the form of the project plan.

Exercise 5.2

Formulate advice and guidelines concerning project planning

Discuss what is good or bad in the way projects are planned in your project or development organization.

Can the advice and guidelines mentioned in Chapter 5 be related to the above-mentioned discussion? What is useful, what is wrong, and what is without importance?

What advice and which guidelines should be spread to other people in the development organization, and how? Work out a table of contents and a number of key messages for a document containing advice and guidelines concerning project planning.

5.5 Estimation — systematic guesswork

Prediction of effort and duration

In practice project planning is often subjected to externally determined estimates of manpower and time consumption. These estimates are not actual estimates but upper limits which are determined by political or financial considerations. This fact often restricts the project and affects the project's plans and working practices in a negative way. One consequence might be that the initial analysis and planning activities are not carried out thoroughly enough: 'If we are going to make it in time, we need to start coding as soon as possible'. The tight time schedules are also justified in psychological considerations: 'Things take the time they are planned to take' and 'Tight time schedules result in more efficient working practices'. These attitudes fail to consider the effect on the quality of the work. The consumption of time and resources is, as already mentioned, a result of a compromise between duration, costs, and quality.

Estimation in our terminology is the evaluation activities which result in a prediction of the project's manpower consumption and the project's duration. Estimation, like most other evaluation activities, is based on personal interpretation and intuition. The many uncertainties

Estimation. Let the estimators choose their own estimation techniques. The more techniques employed, the better.

characterizing system development projects render it difficult to figure out a precise estimate beforehand. The best you can do is to make a qualified guess.

The success of a project depends on whether the planned resources prove sufficient. Because of this, and because it is difficult to make estimates, estimation is an activity which deserves thoroughness. The estimates are based on knowledge about and expectations to the project, as well as on experience from other projects. See Figure 5.10.

Expectations to the project should be expressed in the project plan or in a draft of a plan. Knowledge about the progress of the project so far may be expressed in status reports. Experience from other projects may, among other things, be represented in tables in a textbook, in a specific database in the organization, or in the minds of the system developers.

What characterizes a good estimate?

Estimates should be realistic and convincing

The correctness of an estimate cannot be determined until after the project is concluded. At the time of estimation the decisive criterion is that the estimate is reasonable in relation to the available information. The estimate forms part of the establishment of the project's formal

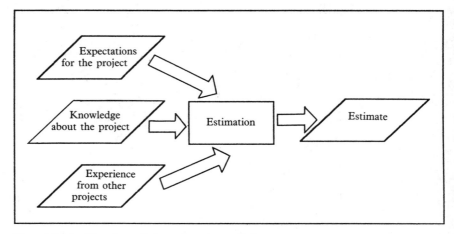

Figure 5.10   The data of the estimation activity.

and informal contracts. In this connection it is important that the estimate is convincing so that everyone participating in the project believes it to be realistic, and so that the development organization or the users cannot undermine it with arguments. An estimate is more convincing if you can account explicitly for how it was worked out, on what experience it is based, and which assumptions were made about the project.

Estimates are uncertain. Therefore it is important that the estimate is accompanied by an assessment of its uncertainty. When planning on the basis of estimates, it is necessary to take this uncertainty into consideration. A plan that collapses because an activity exceeds the estimate, but still lies within the frames of the uncertainty stated in the estimate, is a poor plan.

Advice on and guidelines for estimation

Many system development projects are estimated in a more or less random manner, where experience from other projects only enter implicitly. This will result in unconvincing estimates, and the estimates rarely seem probable. This is an unprofessional way of working. Our principle is that it is necessary to employ supplementary estimation techniques. A plan should be based on a probable estimate, and it should express uncertainties in the estimate (principle M9, Chapter 3).

- Employ different techniques, compare the results, discuss the deviations, and employ the techniques again.

- Split up activities and products, and estimate 'sub-projects'.

- Let the system developers, who are going to perform the activities, estimate them — this will result in better estimates and improve the sense of commitment.

- Let the estimators choose their own estimation techniques. The more techniques employed, the better.

Figure 5.11   Advice on and guidelines for estimation.

There are three different fundamental techniques for systematically working towards a qualified guess of the extent of the project: extrapolation, algorithmic models, and explicit analogy. Figure 5.11 contains some general advice and guidelines about the application of these techniques, and the techniques will subsequently be presented briefly in the following.

Extrapolation

Using extrapolation the extent of an activity is calculated on the basis of the effort in a concluded activity or the size of an intermediate product. Hence the technique is based on the assumption that there is a clear connection between the effort in earlier activities or the size of intermediate products, and the extent of future activities. Extrapolation techniques therefore require that several projects in the same development organization employ the same project model or the same description tools. Extrapolation techniques furthermore require thorough evaluation of whether an activity has been performed, or whether an intermediate product has the desired quality.

Extrapolation requires homogeneous working practices

The advantage of extrapolation is that it offers a reasonable guess of the effort in certain activities, for instance test and repair. However, extrapolation requires homogeneous working practices. This requirement is rarely fulfilled and difficult to meet — and it may often be an inexpedient requirement. Generally the disadvantage of extrapolation is that the technique does not take project-specific factors, like the system developers' qualifications, or the diversity and complexity of the products, into consideration. Extrapolation is furthermore difficult to get started on because it requires that the participants work out their own data on the basis of earlier projects.

Extrapolation may be based on the application of data-flow diagrams as description tools. The extent of an intermediate product may then be measured by the number of elements in a data-flow diagram.

Algorithmic models

In algorithmic models a number of circumstances in the project are evaluated and converted into figures which are put into an arithmetic

---

COCOMO is based on an estimation of the development conditions and the number of code lines (KDSI — kilo delivered source instructions) and the following 15 effort-determining factors:

1. Required software reliability.
2. Data base size.
3. Product complexity.
4. Execution time constraint.
5. Main storage constraint.
6. Change frequency for basic software and hardware.
7. Availability of development computer.
8. System analyst capability.
9. System developers' experience with application.
10. Programmer capability.
11. Experience with basic software and hardware.
12. Programming language experience.
13. Modern working practices.
14. Development tools.
15. Time pressure in the project.

Each of these 15 factors is evaluated and according to a table converted to numerical values. If the system developers, for instance, have 1 year's experience with the programming language, factor 12 will amount to 1.00. If they have 3 years' experience, the factor will be 0.95. If their experience is less than 1 month, the factor will be 1.14.

Different development conditions have different formulae with specific coefficients and powers, so-called productivity constants, which are based on experience from completed projects. With the help of these formulae the effort and duration is estimated.

Under normal development conditions the formula for calculating the consumption of man-months will look as follows:

$$MM = 3.0 \times (KDSI)^{1.12} \times factor\ 1 \times \ldots \times factor\ 15$$

Figure 5.12 COCOMO — constructive cost model.

expression (a formula). The value of this expression constitutes the estimate. The formula is constructed on the basis of experience from earlier projects. The constants in the formula may be altered according to the experience in the organization in question. The estimate of the total extent of the project may be decomposed in activities by means of tables indicating the normal percentage allocation in activities.

Algorithmic models take project-specific factors into account

Algorithmic models have a number of advantages compared to extrapolation. Algorithmic models do not require standardized working practices. On the contrary: they take factors specific to the individual projects into account. Algorithmic models are easy to put to work as there are standard formulae. However, the best estimates are achieved if the formulae are adapted to the local conditions. Algorithmic models furthermore have the advantage that consequences of changed conditions are easy to calculate. It is, for instance, easy to tell management the cost of removing a key person from the project.

The main disadvantage of algorithmic models is the degree of uncertainty when evaluating the factors. Some people find it hard to guess the total number of codelines, which is an important factor in most formulae. Evaluation of other factors depends on who is making the evaluation, and this might result in considerable deviations in the estimate.

The best-documented technique for algorithmic models is COCOMO (Constructive Cost Model), which is described by Barry Boehm. Figure 5.12 gives an outline of the COCOMO technique.

Explict analogy

Explicit analogy requires homogeneous products

In explicit analogy the project is compared to another project which resembles it as regards products and activities. Deviations are considered and the effort is adjusted accordingly. Explicit analogy requires that the development organization makes homogeneous products, or that the project participants have knowledge about a large number of projects. Explicit analogy may result in good and very convincing estimates.

The next section will look at how estimates of the extent of activities can form part of an analysis of the activity network, among other things to identify critical activities.

Exercise 5.3

Evaluate experience with estimation

A development organization has found from experience that it is difficult to produce more than an average of approximately 20 lines COBOL per hour in a project developing a new system. This includes man-hours spent after feasibility study and before conversion in the user organization. This is applied to estimate the consumption of man-hours on the basis of an estimate of the most likely number of code lines in the final product. The explicit analogy technique is employed, assuming that the development environments resemble each other. Uncertainty in the estimate is put at ±20%.

- Find out whether this rule-of-thumb is applicable on the projects of your organization.

- Are there similar rules in your organization? Is it possible to deduce anything from post-calculations on the projects? If not, how can experience be exploited in the future, so that it becomes possible to apply explicit analogy?

5.6 Network analysis — identify the critical activities

Network analysis is a technique which is applied to study the correlation and interdependency between the various activities in a project. Network analysis helps to identify the critical paths. The critical paths constitute bottlenecks in the project, i.e. activities and intermediate states requiring special attention. On the basis of the network analysis the order of the activities may be coordinated in relation to allocation of manpower, consumption of equipment, and the plans of other projects. The technique may be employed on several levels. For instance when planning the whole project, or when planning the work with a single, large module. Network analysis requires that there is an estimate of the duration of each individual activity, and that the interdependency between the activities is indicated. The network analysis hence requires that the project participants have a comprehensive idea of the activity structure and of the duration and resource requirements of the individual activities.

Network analysis brings attention to unrealistic plans

In systems development the activities are often determined on the basis of the course of other activities, or on the basis of new requirements from the environment. This means that network analysis is applicable only to a certain degree in systems development projects. The technique is most suitable in large projects with a well-known application area, and which are based on well-known technology. If these conditions are met, network analysis may give valuable information about critical activities. When first applied, network analysis often demonstrates that a critical path passes the official date of conclusion by several months or years. Situations like that indicate a need for revising the plans in one way or another. The network analysis enforces thorough planning, for instance by comparing the point in time when the project is supposed to stop with the required effort and the available resources, thus drawing attention to unrealistic time schedules.

PERT

Make three different estimates of the duration of an activity:
- *an optimistic*
- *a pessimistic*
- *a likely*

This section presents one of the many almost identical network techniques to be found in literature: PERT (Project Evaluation and Review Technique). This technique takes the uncertainties regarding duration of a given activity into consideration. The technique operates with three different estimates of the duration of each activity: the most optimistic, the most pessimistic, and the most likely. Hence a project group is supposed to come up with three different suggestions for how long they expect an activity to last. This is useful, because otherwise there might be a tendency towards too optimistic planning. The three values also make it easier to assess the reasonability of the estimation later. A deviation from the most likely value is not too serious, while a duration shorter than the most optimistic value or longer than the most pessimistic value is a sign of serious misjudgement.

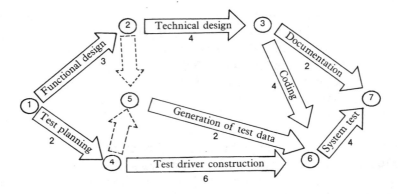

Figure 5.13   Activity network with estimates of the activity duration (below the edges).

Calculation of critical paths

The basis of the calculation is an identification of all the relevant activities and their initial and terminal events, as well as their interdependencies. This may be incorporated in an activity network, for instance with the events represented as nodes and the activities represented as edges between the nodes (a directed graph). Let us assume that these efforts result in the network in Figure 5.13. For technical reasons there can only be one edge (activity) between two nodes (events) in a directed graph. This may entail that nodes with no corresponding event have to be drawn into the graph (for instance node 5 in Figure 5.13) with corresponding 'empty' activities (dotted arrows) which only illustrate dependencies and not an actual activity. The estimates of the duration of activities are denoted below the arrows. The events are numbered with the implied convention that an initial event of an activity always has a lower number than a terminal event.

To find a critical path the graph must be calculated twice. First the graph is calculated from starting date to finishing date. The earliest points in time on which the events can occur are calculated. This will result in Figure 5.14. This is how the minimum time for performing the activities is found — in our case 15.

Then the graph is calculated from finishing time to starting time. Now the latest dates on which the events can occur without increasing the total amount of time necessary to perform all activities in the project are calculated. This will result in Figure 5.15, where each event is

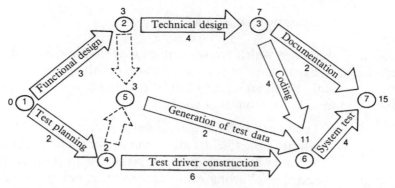

Figure 5.14   Activity network with earliest date for each event (above the nodes).

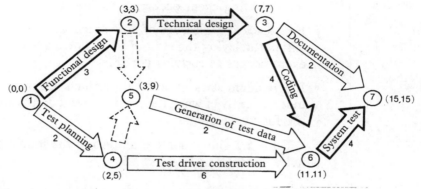

Figure 5.15   Activity network with earliest and latest dates (in brackets).

accompanied by two figures indicating the earliest and the latest dates of each event.

An event where the earliest date of the event equals the latest date is a critical event. A delayed critical event entails that the whole course of the project is prolonged. That is why these events are critical. Edges between critical events with a duration corresponding to the interval between the dates of the two events are critical activities. In the example coding is a critical activity, whereas documentation is not. The critical activities constitute the critical path or paths. There is one critical path in Figure 5.15: functional design, technical design, coding, and system test. Other test activities and documentation are not critical. The critical path is indicated by the dark arrows.

Calculation of slack

*Slack makes it
possible to
handle
unpredicted
changes*

Activities which are not critical may be prolonged or delayed without consequences for the total duration of the project. The length of time with which an activity can be prolonged is called its slack. There are usually four types of slack:

- Total slack is the longest possible prolongation of an activity without affecting the total length of the project. The total slack may be used for other activities if the previous event occurs as early as possible, and the following event can occur as late as possible.

- Safe slack is the safe prolongation of an activity independent of when the previous event has occurred. Using the safe slack may result in the following event occurring as late as possible.

- Free slack is a measure of how much an activity can be prolonged without delaying the start of the following activities if the previous event occurs as early as possible.

- Independent slack indicates how much an activity can be prolonged independently of when the previous event occurs and without delaying the following event.

Table 5.2 shows some examples of the four types of slack in the activity network in Figure 5.15.

Activity	Total slack	Safe slack	Free slack	Independent slack
Test planning	3	3	0	0
Generation of test data	6	0	6	0
Construction of test driver	3	0	3	0
Documentation	6	6	6	6

Table 5.2   Slack in the activity network in Figure 5.15.

Calculation of uncertainties

The above-mentioned calculations have only incorporated the most likely guess at how long an activity will last. PERT assumes that the actual performance time is to be found somewhere between the most optimistic guess and the most pessimistic guess. The assumption is that the actual performance time of an activity will lie close to the likely guess, but instead of the likely guess a calculated value — the average duration — is applied. This value takes into account the distance between the most likely guess on the one hand and the optimistic and pessimistic guesses on the other hand. It is assumed that the performance time of an activity follows a so-called beta distribution. The calculated average durations are incorporated in the network, and the critical paths are found as described above. The standard deviation in the duration of each activity and the critical paths are calculated with the aid of statistical formulae. This will give a rough idea of the degree of uncertainty in the estimate of the total duration of the project. This technique for calculating uncertainties is very rough, and there are more advanced techniques which take the weaknesses in PERT into consideration.

The calculation of critical paths, slacks, and uncertainties can become very comprehensive, even in small projects with simple activity structures. It is therefore expedient to employ a computer system for setting up and calculating activity networks. The next section will discuss the possibilities and limitation in applying software in the planning activities.

5.7 Computer-based planning tools

Computer-based planning systems are becoming more and more common in system development organizations. Software producers offer a number of standard systems, and many large development organizations have developed their own planning systems. There are several good reasons for employing a computer-based planning system, as follows:

- Computer systems ensure that the plans are in writing, and that the plans are easy to update.

- It is possible to print out coherent plans of varying degrees of detail on the basis of a registration of the project's activities and related components.

- It is possible to get help in network analysis and estimation.

- Computer systems facilitate the accumulation of experience, which can be exploited when estimating future projects.

Computer-based planning tools enforce discipline

Computer-based planning systems have other advantages. One is worth stressing: application of software for recording plans and information about actual events requires a high degree of discipline in the planning and follow-up activities. If the recorded data were not completely updated, computer print-outs of reports would be of little or no value, and the computer systems would quietly sink into oblivion. The introduction of computers in planning is often linked to a wish on the part of management to gain better control over the systems development work. Systems development projects are frequently required to produce status reports containing computerized reports including plans of, and information about, the actual course of the project. This enforces a discipline which entails the following points:

- That plans are formulated in writing.
- Completeness in the planning of activities.
- Coherence between plans on different levels.
- That the actual course of events in the project is recorded.

Here, as in other computer systems, the reliability of data depends on whether the reports are or can be used. It is of special importance that the system developers can use the reports when calculating consequences in situations where conditions are changed or the number of activities increased. Registration is performed by the system developers, and they must be motivated to ensure that the data is reliable.

Lack of quality in plans can be concealed in impressive-looking reports

Experience shows that it can be difficult to get computer-based planning systems introduced in a development organization. One of the reasons for this may be that the organization does not have a tradition for working out the detailed and thorough plans which are necessary when employing computer systems. The application of the system then entails a lot of extra work — some of it routine work with registration. Simultaneously the follow-up activities on plans are often inadequate. This will spread doubt in the organization as to the value of reports made on computers. Lack of quality in plans and in the project work as a whole may be concealed behind impressive-looking reports. Discussions on the application of the computer system steal the attention from other and more important problems in project management.

It is recommended that planning is concentrated on working out plans and assessing them in terms of quality, and that as simple tools as possible are used to support the planning activities.

Further reading

The minimum standard for the project plan is based on Munk-Madsen (1985). The standard has been tested and is described in MARS 10 (1985). The section on estimation is based on Hansen and Jensen (1985), which also discusses practical experiences with different techniques. Boehm (1981) contains a description of an algorithmic model. DeMarco (1982) gives some ideas for an extrapolation technique based on the use of data-flow diagrams as system description tools. Literature on network analysis is plentiful, see for instance Elmaghraby (1970).

6 Project evaluation — see the problems in time

Face the situation

6.1 Transparency in process and product
6.2 Systematic project evaluation
6.3 Reviews and technical walkthroughs
6.4 Mapping problematic situations

System development projects involve learning processes to such an extent that they are difficult to predict. Add to this the power struggle often taking place in the development and user organizations, and you will understand why so many project plans fail. Project plans are necessary, but they must be supplemented by evaluations of both the products and the process. One way of improving the predictability of system development projects is to make the projects transparent to the involved participants, thus improving their ability to act in relation to the project. The fundamental principle is that systems development is characterized by a high degree of uncertainty, hence the most important prerequisite of qualified management is transparency in process and products (principle M3, Chapter 3).

This chapter looks at evaluation activities, and introduces a number of techniques and tools which may help to increase the transparency in the project. Section 6.1 gives an example of a project in which much is done to increase the transparency. Section 6.2 discusses how system developers, through systematic project evaluation, can understand what is going on in the project. The rest of the chapter presents techniques for project evaluation. Section 6.3 describes reviews and technical walkthroughs, which are techniques for evaluating product quality. Section 6.4 briefly describes mapping which is a technique for evaluating project situations.

6.1 Transparency in process and product

Thinking in terms of contracts can be a useful means to obtain transparency. The contract concept introduced in Chapter 2 will be briefly summarized.

A system development project may be viewed as consisting of a number of contracts and activities. The contracts link the project participants together as a group and regulate the project's relations to its environment. The contracts are established and regulated through various activities. The contracts consist of external contracts between the project and its environment, primarily the user organization, as well as of internal contracts between the project participants.

The contracts contain agreements about the product, i.e. requirements of the new system. They contain agreements about the process, for instance requirements to the project in the form of deadlines and available resources. Many of the contracts are informal, for instance values, norms, and social relations developed in the project. The formal contracts are written down in design proposals, plans, and minutes.

A project is more or less transparent to a person or a group depending on how easy it is for the person or the group to understand relevant problems and possible actions. Various conditions determine how transparent a project is to the system developers, management of the development organization, or the user organization.

A transparent project is characterized by the fact that the involved parties have knowledge about the contracts, and the fact that they can influence the establishment and regulation of the contracts. Hence it is not enough that the system developers give management and users correct and relevant information about the project. They must also give them time to understand the situation and make decisions. This may easily take a couple of months. All too often you see project plans where one phase is followed closely by the next one containing a decision point but no decision process between the phases. This is wrong. The practical consequence is that even if the first phase is finished on time, the next phase will start with a delay of a couple of months.

Transparency should be established and maintained

Transparency in a project is obtained partly through preventive activities, and partly through activities which aim at maintaining the transparency once the project has started. The preventive activities include project establishment, project planning, and product design. The transparency is improved if the documents resulting from these activities are simple and easy to understand. Another important point is to plan the communication in and around the project from the start, and to incorporate possibilities in the project for evaluating situations. All these measures are described in more detail in other parts of this book (Chapters 4, 5, 7, 8, and 9). In the actual project situation when the project has started, transparency is maintained through continued communication and project evaluation.

Example of project evaluation

In a project the working practices are evaluated half-way through the course of the project. A one-day seminar is arranged, and all the participants make a general evaluation of the project's status beforehand. They also fill in a form evaluating the working practices in the project group. Among other things the form requires the participants to comment on the transparency in the process and the product (see the questions in Figure 6.1).

Transparency in the process results in a better working climate and increased commitment

The project has experimented with working practices. The objective is to obtain a high degree of transparency through a high level of information, openness about sub-activities, and shared decision-making

How are you satisfied with the transparency in the process?

☐ Very satisfied

☐ Satisfied

☐ Fairly satisfied

☐ Not very satisfied

☐ Dissatisfied

How are you satisfied with the transparency in the product?

☐ Very satisfied

☐ Satisfied

☐ Fairly satisfied

☐ Not very satisfied

☐ Dissatisfied

Figure 6.1 Questions in a project evaluation form.

Project management and organization

- Creation of different versions and acceptance test for each version.
- Overall plan for the entire project and detailed plan for each version.
- The project group takes turns as regards responsibility for designing and maintaining the plans.
- Evaluations based on questionnaires of project meetings and working practices in general. Halfway through the project, evaluation in the form of a one-day seminar.
- Collective internal project management.
- Systematic project establishment producing a written project charter.

Descriptions

- Common standard for descriptions of modifications and new program components.
- Formal reviews of descriptions of new program components.
- Informal walkthroughs for other project participants in connection with sub-activities. These should contribute to making the programs homogeneous and to increasing the transparency in the product.

Project group meetings

- Are regarded as an important forum for exchanging information and presenting problems.
- Rolling agenda which is updated and where each item is discussed and put down in order of priority at the meetings.
- The responsibilities of acting as chairman and of taking down minutes is taken in turns.
- Common decisions are made at the project group meeting.
- Information concerning status is used to revise time schedules.
- Decisions are made concerning time schedules and division of work.

Figure 6.2   Descriptions of working practices in the project charter.

and responsibility. The project group has chosen to experiment with various new working practices (see Figure 6.2). The project has especially experimented with the form of the project group meetings. The project group considers the shared internal project management activities to contribute to the transparency in the process. This kind of management has improved the working climate and increased the participants' commitment.

Lack of transparency in the product — why, and what can be done?

At the meeting it turns out that there is a widespread feeling of dissatisfaction with the transparency of the product. This is analysed with the aid of the mapping technique described in Section 6.4. The result of the mapping activity is that the project participants reach a common understanding of the situation, and that they agree on a number of activities which may increase the transparency in the product. The project participants' understanding of the situation is documented in Figure 6.3.

Lack of transparency.

What is the problem?

Lack of transparency in the product:
• Lack of understanding of the dependencies between sub-products.
• Unclear status.
• Specialization in the work.
• Uncertainty as regards the complexity of future activities.

Why did it happen?

• Too few joint meetings when the activities started, lack of specifications of changes
  — overall specifications only in headlines.
• Intention of the project charter not observed.
• Lack of discipline at the first meetings.

What are the consequences?

• Uncertainty about the importance and consequences of design decisions.
• Poor training in the course of the project as regards installation, etc.
• Increased specialization.
• Poorer starting point for new design decisions.

What can we do?

• Formalize the meetings when the activities are started (the meetings should include
  re-evaluation of time consumption and time of conclusion).
• Do regular follow-up on the project plan at project group meetings.
• Make better preparations when activities are started.

Figure 6.3   Analysis of the problem: lack of transparency in the product.

This is an illustration of a project making an effort to increase the transparency in both process and product. The project was organized from the start to reach this goal. The project was established systematically, and this has, among other things, resulted in a thorough plan stipulating frequent evaluations of the working process. The organization of the project serves to increase the transparency by preventing the negative effects of a one-sided specialization. Finally the transparency of the product is promoted through incremental development, walkthroughs, standards, and reviews.

The thorough common preparations in themselves increase the transparency in the project, and they also increase the chances of seeing and solving problems surfacing in the course of the project. When the project group sees the problem of the lacking transparency in the product this is, among other things, due to the transparency in the process.

The example described concerns transparency in the project group. Both management of the development organization and other interested parties obviously also benefit from a transparent project. These parties are heavily dependent on whether the project group plans and organizes the project in a manner which allows them to act meaningfully in relation to the project.

Exercise 6.1

Evaluate your experience as regards transparency

- How would the working practices in the above-mentioned project work in your project (see Figure 6.2)? List some advantages and some disadvantages.
- How is the transparency in your project? List some positive and some negative situations.
- Do you recognize the problem in Figure 6.3 in your project? Supplement with other causes, effects, and suggestions.
- List some other problems you think ought to be analysed in the project group. Employ the pattern in Figure 6.3.
- Suggest alternative working practices in your project on the basis of this example.

System developers are often seen as objective experts working towards the organization's common goals. In reality system developers are people with personal likes and dislikes, with political attitudes and professional ambitions. They might therefore have an interest in making the project transparent to parties who may influence the project. Otherwise they might risk that decisions are taken on the basis of too little or even wrong information. In other situations, however, system developers might have an interest in playing a more passive role to let other groups or actors handle conflicts or problems between themselves.

The remaining part of this chapter discusses how system developers through systematic project evaluation ensure that they themselves understand what is happening in the project.

6.2 Systematic project evaluation

The objective of project evaluation is to create an understanding of a project situation. This understanding forms the basis for planning and regulation. In practice project evaluation will often take place in processes in which another activity is on the agenda, along the following lines:

- At the end of a phase when the project group starts to plan the next phase in detail, they will ask themselves: Did we do the things we expected to do in this phase? Did we learn something new about the conditions of the project? How will this influence the next phase?

- When the project group designs a data base they ask themselves: Do we know enough about the data-base management system? Should we make the design flexible, so that we can experiment with it?

- When the project group wishes to increase the commitment among its participants, this can be done in a session at a project group meeting where everyone in turn answers the questions: What have I accomplished? What do I still need to do?

Answering these questions is project evaluation. However, in the examples project evaluation only constitutes a supportive activity in

Plan without evaluation. Evaluation and planning are mutually dependent, and should therefore be performed concurrently.

It is important to create a precise picture of the project

relation to the main activity, i.e. planning, design, and regulation, respectively.

What really makes project evaluation difficult is that it is often performed in connection with other activities, and that it would be unfortunate if the evaluation delays or disturbs these other activities. However, it is necessary that professional management of a system development project creates a picture of the project which is as precise as possible. That is why project evaluation should be taken seriously and studied as an activity in itself.

Project evaluation may be initiated primarily on the basis of two objectives. First, you may wish to ensure that the actual situation is as expected before you continue the work. In situations like that you need a type of project evaluation which will be called a routine check. Secondly, an unforeseen problematic situation may have surfaced in the project which you do not understand or do not know how to handle. In situations like that you need a type of project evaluation which will be called problem analysis.

The working practices to be applied in project evaluation may be described in the form of techniques. Literature on management of systems development projects especially deal with techniques to be employed in routine check situations, including techniques dealing with quantitative questions. This may draw the system developers' attention away from qualitative questions and from how project evaluation is performed in problematic situations. These questions are, however, not the least important ones.

Routine check

Routine checks are carried out to ensure the following points:

- That the expectations for the project, as they are expressed in the plan, are logically coherent.

- That the products and services produced are in accordance with the expectations.

- That the current activities follow the plan.

- That the consumption of resources follows the plan.

- That the conditions under which the work is carried out still prevail.

The expectations for the project should be expressed in the project plan. If the plan is not good enough, or if there are signs that groups related to the project have expectations deviating from the plan, the project is out of balance, and the project is in a problematic situation. The situation is then a problem analysis one instead of a routine check. In routine check situations we assume that the expectations to the project are documented in such a way that it is possible, on the basis of the plan, to determine first whether the expectations are logically coherent, and secondly whether the expectations are in accordance with reality.

Evaluation of qualitative coherence is a neglected issue

There are various techniques for evaluating the coherence in the project plan. Some of them are suitable for evaluating quantitative coherence. One of these techniques is network analysis, which is suitable for examining the temporal correlation between the activities in the project. Another technique is estimation, which deals with the relation between product size, the extent of activities, and the number of resources. (Network analysis and estimation are described in more detail in Chapter 5.) Another type of question in connection with evaluation of the internal coherence in a project plan deals with qualitative coherence, for instance whether there is sufficient interaction between

	Reviews	Self-registration	Inspection	Interview	Test
Resources	–	+ +	+	+	+
Conditions	–	+	+	+	–
Organization	–	+	+	+	–
Activities	–	+	+ +	+	–
Products	+ +	–	+	–	+ +
Services	–	–	+	+	+ +
Side effects	–	–	+	+ +	–

Notes:
+ + Suitable.
  + Suitable in some cases.
 – Unsuitable.

Table 6.1   The suitability of various techniques for routine checking of the project plan's accordance with reality.

the analysis of the user organization and the design of the computer system, or whether there is sufficient communication in and around the project. Evaluation of qualitative coherence may be based on statements of the type expressed in the principles in Chapter 3.

Evaluation of whether the plan is in accordance with reality includes investigation of the following components: resources, conditions, organization, activities, products, services, and side-effects. For this purpose there are a number of techniques: reviews, self-registration, inspection, interview, and test. These techniques are of varying suitability for elucidating the questions concerning the various components. Table 6.1 roughly describes the suitability of the techniques.

A review is a thoroughly prepared meeting where the quality of a product is evaluated. Reviews are discussed in more detail in Section 6.3. Self-registration is suitable for documenting quantitative information about the consumption of resources. The most obvious examples are computers which automatically register the consumption of machine resources, and project participants who fill in time sheets. Qualitative information may be documented by system developers keeping a diary. Inspection is an activity where a person examines a specific situation. This may be done by reading documents or through direct observation. Interviews are more or less structured discussions between two parties where the discussion is determined by the party that needs information.

*The project
plan should
include
descriptions of
baselines*

Tests, as the word indicates, are tests of products, services, and, in some cases, resources performed in artificial environments.

Experience indicates that it is easier to evaluate the consumption of resources, available products and intermediate products than to evaluate current or finished activities. It is therefore recommended that the project plan includes a description of baselines and checkpoints where intermediate products must have reached a certain state (see Chapter 7). Baseline descriptions should include evaluation criteria and procedures. Thus they entail a number of routine checks in connection with the planned checkpoints (principle M6, Chapter 3).

Problem analysis

Problem analysis takes its starting point in acknowledgement of something being wrong in the project. The task here is primarily to analyse the situation to reveal one or more problems and get inspiration to regulate the situation.

To begin with the problem is rarely well-defined. Different people have different ideas of what is wrong and what should be done about it. The objective is to create a common understanding of the project situation and of the central problems. The result may be that the participants fail to reach a common understanding of the problem. However, it is important to discuss the project situation and problems thoroughly. Otherwise there is a risk of starting to solve pseudo-problems, or of keeping on working with unprocessed conflicts. Problem analysis must always take place in a dialogue between the people involved. Section 6.4 presents some techniques for analysis of problematic situations.

Interaction with planning and regulation

So far we have dealt with project evaluation as an independent separate activity. This has been necessary to be able to discuss the various techniques. In practice, however, project evaluation will be closely linked to the other parts of project management, i.e. planning and regulation.

It is a principle that evaluation and planning are mutually dependent, and should therefore be performed concurrently in order to support each other (principle M1, Chapter 3). Another principle is that process-oriented reflection (planning and evaluation) and regulation affect each other, and they should therefore be performed concurrently in order to support each other (principle M2, Chapter 3).

Project evaluation should be the responsibility of the system developers

Outsiders can assess the quality of status reports. It is, however, difficult for outsiders to assess the state of a system development project while it is under progress. One reason is that the close interaction between management activities requires that many evaluation activities have to be the responsibility of those engaged, i.e. the system developers themselves. Another reason is that only the system developers have enough insight into all the details. Project management is thus an important activity for system developers, and a prerequisite of performing this activity in a professional manner is that the system developers master the concrete techniques for project evaluation. The remaining part of this chapter discusses project evaluation techniques.

Exercise 6.2

Assess the project evaluation activity

- Which types of project evaluation have you undertaken in your current project?
- Who undertakes the project evaluation activity?
- Who follows up on it?
- Should project evaluation activities in your project be strengthened?

6.3 Reviews and technical walkthroughs

Reviews

A review is a meeting where the quality of a product is evaluated. Now, you may ask: 'So what? We have lots of meetings where we discuss products. So why give the meetings a special name?' There are two answers to this. First, most meetings where products are discussed deal with the design of the future product. What makes reviews different is that they are held after the product is finished with the objective of evaluating the quality of the product. Meetings like that are far from common in system development projects. Secondly, the review technique includes some guidelines which ensure efficient evaluation.

These guidelines will be presented in the following. The guidelines are inspired by Freedman and Weinberg's book on evaluation techniques. Chapter 12 contains an example of practical application of the review technique.

The reviewer should point out problems — not solve them

A review has four objectives: To point out the need for improvements, if there are any; to approve a product; to create homogeneous quality; and to train. These objectives should be taken literally. It is the reviewer's responsibility to point out problems — not to solve them. It is the quality of the product which should be evaluated — not how it was produced. When we speak of products here we mean end-products (for instance source text, user manuals, maintenance documentation) and intermediate products (for instance project plans, analysis reports, design documents). All these products can be reviewed.

The course of a review is described in Figure 6.4. Before the actual review the reviewers should have time to study the product and compare it with the requirements. The review itself should not be longer than two hours. If it is impossible to get through all the material in two hours, there should be several reviews. The number of participants in a review should be between three and seven. The reviewers should be technically competent in relation to the product. They must not be participants in the project group which made the product. Most important of all they must not be managers of the producers.

If the review turns out to become unsuccessful, the review leader should interrupt the meeting

A review leader is appointed beforehand. The review leader is responsible for creating a good review, or to report why this was not possible. The review leader should ensure that the product is finished and distributed to the reviewers, that they are prepared, and that the meetings are conducted at a suitable pace, that the discussions stick to the issue, and that the meeting is interrupted if the prerequisites are not met.

A recorder is also appointed beforehand. The recorder is responsible for creating the basis of the review report. During the review the recorder should write the main points on a blackboard and details on a piece of paper. The recorder should work out a conclusion on the basis of the meeting.

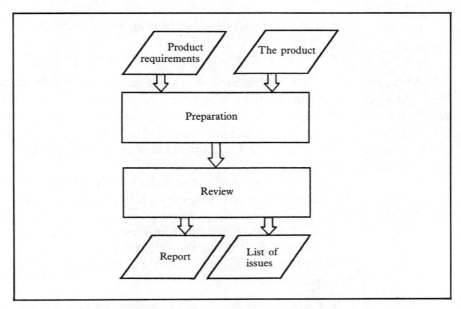

Figure 6.4   The course of a review.

Every reviewer should be well prepared. It is important that each reviewer puts forward both positive and negative comments. The reviewers should point out problems and raise issues, but not suggest solutions. In particular, style is one of the things that should not be discussed. It is the product that should be evaluated, not the production process or the personal qualities of the producers.

The producers are responsible for listening to what is being said, and to answer questions, not to come up with excuses or explanations. Note that it is the producers who decide when a product is ready for review.

A review results in a report and a list of issues. The report is in writing and is public. The report should answer the question: Is the product good enough? There are five possible answers to that question, as follows:

- The product is approved without any comments.
- The product is approved after a few minor corrections. Another review is superfluous.
- The product is not approved; major corrections are necessary, and a new review.

- The product is useless; management must decide what should be done.
- The review could not be carried through.

*The reviewers
are responsible
for the report;
the producers
are responsible
for the product*

The reviewers should agree on the conclusion. If they cannot reach agreement, they must conclude that the review could not be carried through. The reviewers are responsible for the quality of the report, the producers are responsible for the product. Should it turn out later that an approved product has serious errors or defects, it is an insufficient excuse that there was a review.

Problems, errors, and defects pointed out during the review are taken down in an enclosure — a list of problems — which is given to the producers. If the review reveals circumstances which affect other parts of the development organization, this is taken down in notes which are then passed on to the relevant people.

There are a number of other guidelines for reviews. The three most important are as follows:

- Leave room and time in the project plan for reviews.

- Make sure that at least one person (preferably the review leader) knows Freedman and Weinberg's book.

- Build up your own traditions.

Figure 6.5 gives an example from a company which has worked out its own advice and guidelines for reviews.

Technical walkthroughs

The most important difference between reviews and technical walkthroughs is that there are external people involved in the former, and that written material is available which has been read and evaluated by the participants beforehand. Only people from the project participate in technical walkthroughs, and there is not necessarily distributed any written material beforehand.

As in reviews the objective is to get criticism. The product which is present to the other project members would typically be a detailed design proposal. As opposed to reviews, technical walkthroughs may result in suggestions for new or altered solutions.

Technical walkthroughs will entail that specialization in the project group is smoothed out, and that the individual project participants obtain

Review — of what?

Reviews of more general, complete descriptions are recommended — for instance:
• User-oriented descriptions.
• Overall designs.
• Manuals.

Apart from that reviews may be arranged of process descriptions — for instance:
• The project charter.
• The project plan.

Review — by whom?

The following 'actors' participate in the review:
• The leader of the review (brought in from outside the project).
• The recorder (project participant).
• Producers.
• External reviewers (brought in from outside the project).

The leader of the review should be relatively strict so that the meeting does not exceed the allocated time.

The recorder should have insight into the project so that the minutes will contain the important issues discussed at the meeting.

The external reviewers should be technically competent and be able to criticize the produced material in a positive manner.

It is often a good idea that the project participants are present at the meeting and act as observers. The observers should be passive and not participate in the discussions.

Figure 6.5   Extracts from a company's advice and guidelines for reviews.

Technical walkthroughs result in discussions among the project participants

a better understanding of each other's work. Technical walkthroughs will also result in more openness and transparency in the project. All these things will help to increase commitment to the project as a whole.

In a technical walkthrough the producer goes through the description step by step. The objective of the walkthrough is to encourage discussions among the project participants. A recorder might be appointed, but usually the producer himself is responsible for writing down the essence of the discussion as no official report is worked out. If the technical walkthrough is expected to end up with a decision, it is a good idea to distribute descriptions of alternatives beforehand, so that the participants can make preparations.

As with reviews it is a good idea to build up your own traditions (see Figure 6.6).

Technical walkthroughs — of what?

Generally technical walkthroughs of descriptions are recommended when it would require too much effort from people outside the project to understand the description. This often applies to descriptions such as the following:
- Detailed specifications.
- Specifications of changes.
- Programs.
- Suggestions for alternative solutions.

Technical walk-throughs are also recommended for process descriptions such as the following:
- Detailed plans.
- Project charters.

Technical walkthroughs — by whom?

Only project participants take part in the technical walkthrough.

Not all project participants need necessarily take part in the technical walkthrough. However, a minimum requirement is that producers and project participants working with interfaces to the product in question participate.

It is a good idea for more people than those directly involved to take part, as the educational effect is considerable.

Figure 6.6   Extract from a company's advice and guidelines for technical walkthroughs.

6.4 Mapping problematic situations

A system development project may find itself in a situation where some of the participants have a feeling that something is wrong. However, the participants do not know what it is, and there might even be disagreement on whether something is wrong at all. Typical for a situation like that is that people conceive the situation differently, and the air is thick with ideas for solutions, problem formulations, and explanations.

The professional system developer will ask: How do we get the situation under control? This question has two aspects. One is analytically constructive: how do we understand the situation and work out a plan for getting out of it? The other is communicative and regulative: how do we create a common attitude in the project group as a basis for the future work?

This section presents a technique which is called mapping. Mapping is especially suitable in problematic situations such as the one described above. Before we present the technique we give an example of a situation where the technique could be employed.

Map the situation, define the problem

A system development project has just finished a report which contains the overall design of the future system, and a plan for the rest of the project. This report has been approved by the project steering committee. At this point there is a project group meeting where some of the participants criticize the report. They maintain that the report is deficient and incoherent. The project leader's reply is that this might be true, but the steering committee has, after all, approved the report. Later the meeting develops into a discussion of details in the report. The result of the meeting is that no changes are made in the project. Later, as could be anticipated, the project runs into difficulties. What should the project group have done on this meeting? They could have mapped the situation and defined the problem as a starting point for new planning activities.

A problematic situation may be mapped in three different ways:

Problem setting. In problem-setting situations the whole situation is unclear.

- A diagnostic map describes the problem, its causes and consequences, and the alternative actions which should have been taken to prevent the problem from arising.

- An ecological map describes the relation between the situation to be understood and changed, and the organization in which the situation arose.

- A virtual map describes what the project wishes to obtain, what actions should be taken to succeed, and whether the suggested actions actually result in better situations.

The maps are the visible results of mapping. However, they are not the most important result. What is most important is the knowledge the participants obtain through the mapping process. Mapping should therefore be carried out by those people who are or have been involved in the problematic situation. In the following we will go through the three types of maps.

Diagnostic maps

A diagnostic map describes a problematic situation as experienced and explained by the people involved in it. A diagnostic map may be drawn as shown in Table 6.2, for instance on a blackboard, with columns with the following headings: What is the problem? What causes the problem? What are the consequences of the problem? What are the alternatives?

Problem	Causes	Consequences	Alternatives
• The overall design is inadequate, but the steering committee expects the project group to continue.	• Inadequate analysis and design techniques. • Observing the deadlines has too high priority.	• Inadequate basis for detailed design. • The product is unclear to the users, and they will request changes.	• Realistic time schedule. • Better analysis and design techniques. • Lower level of ambition.

Table 6.2 Example of a diagnostic map.

The idea behind the technique is that the individual participants try to classify their statements about the situation under one of the four headings, while they simultaneously explain causal relations and, as far as possible, base their statements on established facts. As the table is filled in the participants examine whether the statements are coherent. Do the causes contradict each other? Are the consequences serious, and do they confirm the seriousness of the problem? Why do people believe in the alternatives? What would the alternative situation have been? If the statements are contradicting, the project group discusses whether this is due to incorrect interpretations which can be corrected, or whether the contradictions can be explained by the fact that different people have different conceptions of the situation. If the latter is the case, this should be investigated in a new map.

The success of the technique depends on whether the project group finds a good way to formulate the problem. A good problem formulation contains a contradiction. A solution to the problem should resolve or handle this contradiction. (See Figure 6.7.)

The discussion should be balanced   The strength of diagnostic maps is that they help to understand and communicate the problem. They help the project participants to understand how their fellow participants see the situation. Diagnostic maps also help the project group to obtain a shared understanding of the situation. The description of the project situation should cover major positive and negative characteristics. This is of considerable psychological value. The main objects of the discussion are the participants, their actions, and their products. Even if 90% of a product is good, the atmosphere would soon become discouraging if only the 10% containing more or less insoluble problems were discussed. It is important to document the positive aspects so that you can see whether a suggestion for solving the defined problems will create new problems by ruining other, positive aspects.

A formulation of a problem is good if:

- It contains a contradiction.
- The problem causes many other contradictions in the map.
- It points towards solutions (cure is better than prevention).
- It is relatively well-documented by evidence.

Figure 6.7   Criteria for evaluating formulations of problems.

Ecological maps

*Get an
overview of the
internal and
external
conditions*

Ecological maps describe the relations between acknowledged problems and the internal and external conditions in the organization. Internal conditions are circumstances which the participants can regulate themselves, while external conditions describe the circumstances which are primarily determined by the surroundings, and which the participants only can influence to a certain degree. Whether a condition is registered as internal or external thus depends on who participates in the mapping activity, and also on what the participants' believe they can influence.

Figure 6.8 illustrates how the situation we described in Table 6.2 could be described in an ecological map.

Ecological maps may be produced in the same way as diagnostic maps by drawing columns on a blackboard and letting the participants discuss what should be written in the individual columns. The dotted arrows in Figure 6.8 illustrate that the conditions form and delimit what

External conditions

- The steering committee expects success.
- Unrealistic time schedules.
- The system developers are not working full-time on the project because the development organization requires them to maintain old systems simultaneously.

Situation

- The overall design is defective.
- The project goes ahead on the basis of the overall design.

Internal conditions

- The system developers do not expect to have any influence on the time schedule.
- The system developers do not impose their will on the project leader and the steering committee.
- Very few informal contacts with the users.

Figure 6.8   Example of an ecological map.

happens and can happen in the situation, while the full arrows illustrate that the participants' actions can influence the conditions. Ecological maps serve to group the conditions into action domains so that it is possible to discuss what conditions can be changed when, by whom, and how.

Virtual maps

Evaluate possible actions

Virtual maps are employed to describe possible and desirable future actions and situations. They illustrate actions which can be simulated and tested before they are put into effect to regulate the situation. The maps help to evaluate the consequences of actions and options before these actions and options are put into effect. They help to clarify how you can move from the present problematic situation to a more desirable one. They force the participants to answer the question: 'What will happen if we do this or that?'

A virtual map can be drawn up in the same way as a diagnostic map, but while the diagnostic map points backwards and aims at processing experience, the virtual map points forward and aims at bringing the participants out of a current problematic situation.

Mapping with virtual maps includes answering the following questions:

- What do we want? The participants imagine how they would like to see the future progress of the project.

- What can we do? On the basis of what the participants imagine would be a desirable future project situation, they discuss what actions would be necessary to undertake to reach this project situation.

- What are the consequences? The participants evaluate what the consequences would be of putting the proposed actions into effect.

- Will we gain what we hoped for? The participants evaluate whether the actions actually will result in a better situation than the present one.

Mapping with virtual maps is a process in which wishes and actions are discussed until more advantageous situations seem obtainable.

Mapping includes planning, evaluation, and regulation

There is a close link between diagnostic and ecological maps. You will typically be able to identify the conditions in an ecological map by looking for the causes and consequences in a diagnostic map. There is also a connection between these two types of maps and virtual maps. Understanding a problematic situation and its conditions is the basis for creating the visions of a desired situation, and how this situation is obtained.

Employing maps helps to ensure that the necessary interaction between planning, evaluation, and regulation is established in practice. Mapping starts as an evaluation activity, but the considerations concerning alternatives and how they can be put into effect turn mapping into a planning activity. Mapping finally changes the participants' qualifications, attitudes, and expectations, thus forming the basis for changing conditions and working practices. Hence the regulation activities are initiated.

Exercise 6.3

Map some situations

Map some problematic situations in your current project.

Persuade the rest of your project group to do the same.

Compare your individual maps and draw up some common maps.

Further reading

The example concerning project evaluation in Section 6.1 is described in more detail in MARS 3 (1984). The division of project evaluation situations into routine checks and problem analysis is based on Munk-Madsen (1985). Section 6.3 on reviews and technical walkthroughs is based on Freedman and Weinberg (1982), and Section 6.4 on mapping is based on Lanzara and Mathiassen (1985).

7 Baselines improve project management

Shared fixed points between actors support effective action

The size of systems development projects usually requires that the project work is divided into comprehensible parts. The system developers need others to respond to the quality of their work — they need to feel 'the moment of truth', and they need fixed points in the internal coordination. The development organization and the user organization need to know the state of the project, and they need to evaluate whether the project is on the right track. The project work should be carried out in a manner that allows for these needs.

It is important to plan with points in time in the course of the project where the overall state of the project can be evaluated. The plan should focus on descriptions of desirable states. These descriptions form the basis of evaluating the state of the project — has the desired state actually been achieved? The concept baseline is used to focus on project states. Figure 7.1 gives our definition of a project baseline.

Baselines form a better basis for project management than phases

Project work is traditionally divided into a number of temporally separated parts, so-called phases, in which certain types of activities are to be performed. A phase is concluded with a report describing the results of the phase. The report also forms the decision basis for the future work in the project. There are many examples of projects where the actual state was not evaluated at the end of a phase. One reason for this is that the criteria for an evaluation are not present. The conclusion of a phase failed to act as 'the moment of truth' or as a fixed point facilitating local planning. It is our experience that descriptions of baselines in a project plan create a better basis for project management than do the traditional descriptions of phases. The project should, however, still be divided into phases, even when project management is based on baselines. Thus the idea is not to move away from division into phases, but to structure the course of the project in a new way as regards contents.

Section 7.1 describes the idea of baselines in more detail. The value of baselines is pointed out and some examples are presented of baselines and lack of baselines. Section 7.2 describes a number of important

---

A baseline is a project state which is thoroughly described in a plan.

A project has reached a baseline when intermediate products are in well-defined states and other important prerequisites are known.

A baseline is a coordinated project state which everyone in the project can refer to.

Figure 7.1 Definition of a project baseline.

intermediate products which ought to enter into baselines. Section 7.3 deals with project management employing baselines. How do you plan with the help of baselines, and how can you evaluate on the basis of baselines? Section 7.4 introduces the concept of configuration management which deals with managing the state of the products.

7.1 Use baselines

Systems development projects are complicated and characterized by a strong need for internal coordination. A project easily comes to a standstill if there are too many interdependencies and uncertainties about what other project participants are doing. Local planning — and thus the management of the project — would be strengthened if everyone in the project could refer to a well-known point of departure. A baseline is such a well-known point of departure to which everyone can refer.

Traditionally baselines denote well-defined product states, but in our terminology baselines more broadly refer to project states. A baseline is thoroughly described in a plan. In particular the state of intermediate products, but also the prerequisites of the future work, should be described. A baseline is a project state to which everyone in the project can refer. A baseline permits continued progress in the project without too high communication and coordination costs. That is why not all project states are baselines.

Lacking baselines

The importance of baselines can be illustrated by looking at a project that works without baselines. The project's internal plan states that the end of a specific phase should result in an overall technical design which should form the basis for the work in the following phases. When the time set aside for the phase is spent, the project group realizes that only the following things are available:

- A design layout made quite early in the project.
- A number of minutes of meetings where design decisions have been made.

- A number of notes describing solutions of special problems.

There are important decisions and prerequisites which have not been taken down in writing. They only exist in the minds of some of the system developers.

The overall technical design is an intermediate product which should have been available at the end of the phase. Has the project reached the state it should? The existing number of descriptions cannot be presented to anyone outside the project. The project group has no opportunity to obtain comments on the product (whether the design could have been made in a smarter way), or on the process (whether the design is good enough to continue to work on).

The project group hurries on and tells the world that the project is on schedule. The project group thus avoids negotiating with development management and with the users about changing the plans. The project group is also convinced that they will be able to complete the system. Thus it would be a waste of time to polish an intermediate product which, after all, will be discarded when the system and the proper documentation are finished.

Test and conversion always reveals the truth

The project steering committee approves the end of a phase, but the project group does not establish a baseline with well-defined product states. The project has failed to establish a common frame of reference concerning the design of the product. Later in the project, during the test of the whole system, it turns out that one of the programs fails to deliver the data which another program expects. This interface has not been written down, and it turns out that the two programmers disagree on what the interface should be. They also disagree on which program should be altered. At the same time it turns out that changes have been made in a system delivering data to the new system. No one has talked with the people who are responsible for maintaining that system. The required alterations prove so extensive that the time schedule no longer can be met. The first 'moment of truth' in the project is revealed during the test of the whole system.

Another 'moment of truth' should be the point in time when the overall technical design is supposed to be ready. In the present example the project group should have created the common frame of reference which the overall design constitutes. Maybe the project group forgot to describe the interface which later caused the problems, but this would have been revealed when the first programmer started to design his program in detail on the basis of the overall design.

The project group should have clarified the prerequisites, and thus made the necessary agreements about changes in the basic system. Having no overall technical design baseline, the project group missed the encouragement of seeing the concrete results of its work.

The alternative to the situation described above is for the project group to negotiate with development management and with the users for more time to finish the overall design. However, which criteria should they have used to evaluate whether the design was finished? This should have been made clear in the project plan.

Description of baselines

The above-mentioned example illustrates how important it is to make thorough plans and evaluations of desired product states. Figure 7.2 suggests a template for how to describe a baseline which will help to make these plans and evaluations.

Describe evaluation criteria and procedures

It is a principle that project plans should facilitate evaluations. Thus it is important that a description of a baseline contains evaluation criteria and procedures (principle M6, Chapter 3). In the example above the project group continues its work without determining whether the planned intermediate state has been reached, and without considering

- Name of baseline

- List of
  (a) Intermediate products in specific states.
  (b) Other important prerequisites of the future work.

- Criteria for evaluation:
  (a) characteristics of intermediate products, resources, user organization, etc.

- Procedures for evaluation:
  (a) How should the project be evaluated (review, test, etc.)?
  (b) Who should evaluate?
  (c) Who are the decision-makers?

Figure 7.2   Template for describing a baseline.

Baseline: The overall design has been completed.

Consists of the following:

- Overall functional design has been completed.
- Overall technical design has been completed.
- A prototype of screen display dialogue has been developed and tested in cooperation with the users.
- Plan for realizing the design has been completed.
- Agreements with all the involved parties have been established.
- The user organization agrees to the overall design and the plan.

Criteria for evaluation:

- The functional and technical designs meet the minimum standard (see suggestion in Section 7.2).
- The prototype is in accordance with the functional design.
- The plan meets the minimum standard (see suggestion in Chapter 5).
- The prerequisites of the plan are fulfilled.
- The user organization has worked out a booklet about the new system and the consequent changes. This has been done on the basis of overall design. The booklet is in accordance with the other intermediate products.

Procedures for evaluation:

- There have been reviews and technical walkthroughs of prototypes, overall functional design, overall technical design and the project plan; the pupose of these is to ensure that the criteria have been fulfilled.
- The affected parties have been interviewed in order to evaluate whether the prerequisites in the plan are fulfilled.
- The user organization's booklet has been reviewed in order to evaluate whether the booklet is in accordance with the overall design and the plan.

Figure 7.3   Example of a description of a baseline.

the consequences. There were no evaluation criteria for the overall technical design, and the only procedure for evaluation was a requirement that the steering committee must approve the conclusion of the phase and the initiation of the next phase. However, the steering committee has no opportunity to evaluate the quality of the overall technical design. Figure 7.3 gives an example of a description of a baseline where the overall design enters as an intermediate product.

Section 7.3 will describe how a baseline can be employed in project management. But first we will discuss which intermediate products are important in a systems development project, thus becoming candidates for entering into baselines.

Exercise 7.1

Use of baselines

Try to use baselines in your next project.

- Describe desirable baselines.
- Determine the points in time when the baselines should be reached.
- Evaluate whether the baselines have been reached.
- Revise the plans according to the actual situation.

7.2 Important intermediate products

The project delivers products and services

What are the intermediate products of a system development project? At the end of the project the actual deliveries are seen. These deliveries can be divided into products and services. A product (for instance executable code and documentation) is a physical object. A service (for instance training and conversion) is an activity running over a period of time which can only be performed by certain people. Figure 7.4 contains a list of the most important deliveries of systems development.

During the project there have been various products and services in various intermediate states. There have been preliminary versions of sub-products of varying quality. Before then there have been more or less detailed, and more or less completed, descriptions of sub-products. Where the services are concerned there have been more or less detailed plans. Some of the services may have been tested.

A systems development project also contains intermediate products which cannot be described as forerunners of the final deliveries. These products include descriptions of the user organization (from the analysis), and documents describing work processes in the project, for instance the project plan (see Chapter 5) and the project charter (see Chapter 4). There may also appear documents evaluating the consequences of the design or of specific choices as regards working practices in the project. Sometimes documents containing analysis of the prerequisites of the design will be produced.

Software

- Source code.
- Executable code.
- Database definitions.
- Job control language commands.

Manuals

- Maintenance documentation.
- Operation documentation.
- User manual.

Services

- Technical conversion (introduction into technical environment), including the following:
  (a) Training the operators.
  (b) Installation.
  (c) Data conversion.
  (d) Preservation of interfaces.

- Functional conversion (introduction into the user organization), including the following:
  (a) Training the users.
  (b) Changing the manual system.
  (c) Data conversion.
  (d) Preservation of interfaces.

Figure 7.4 The deliveries of systems development.

Plan the
intermediate
products on the
basis of the
project situation

It is not possible to make a general standard of important intermediate products and intermediate states. The products, the projects, and the projects' environments are too different for that. It may be impossible, and often inexpedient, even within the individual development organization, to make standards of which intermediate products should be produced in a systems development project, and what intermediate states should be obtained in a project. Figure 7.5 contains a checklist of possible intermediate products. The list may be used as an inspiration when planning intermediate products and baselines. The authors think that there are some intermediate products which should always be made as a consequence of the nature of systems development. These intermediate products are accentuated in Figure 7.5.

There are many standard proposals for intermediate products. It is worth taking a closer look at one important intermediate product,

---

The project charter

The project plan

Status reports
Design drafts, prototypes

Analysis reports

The overall functional design

The overall technical design

Product standards

Test plans

Plan for technical conversion

Plan for functional conversion

Database descriptions
Detailed technical design, basis for programming
Programming tools developed in the project
Test data

Preliminary versions of the project deliveries   (see Figure 7.4)

Evaluation of the project after it has been completed

Figure 7.5 Checklist of intermediate products. The products written in bold type should always be produced.

namely the overall design and an important, but often neglected, end-product, namely the maintenance documentation.

The overall design

The most important intermediate products

It is a principle that the project plan and the overall design are the most important intermediate products of a systems development project (principle PM2, Chapter 3). They form the common frame of reference for the project. The plan is the key document in relation to the process, and the design is the key document in relation to the product. The quality of these intermediate products is decisive for coordination, both internally in the project group, but also between the project group and the surrounding world. Chapter 5 contains a proposal for a minimum standard of the project plan. Figures 7.6 and 7.7 contain proposals for the overall design.

Contents

- Outline of the user organization's functions.
- Outline of important conditions in the user organization, for instance work environment requirements.
- Requirements of the following attributes of the computer system:
  (a) Functionality:
      (i)   Screen displays and print lists determined at field level.
      (ii) The command semantics.
      (iii) The data semantics.
  (b) Capacity.
  (c) Response time.
  (d) Ergonomics.
  (e) Security.
- Description of new work procedures where the future computer systems are used as tools, including changes compared to present working practices.
- Plan for functional conversion.
- Evaluation of important consequences, for instance concerning economy and work environment.

Form

- On the basis of several perspectives (preferably with a combination of graphics and textual descriptions).

Functionality

- For the users to respond to — is this what they want?
- For the system developers to respond to — is it met by the technical design?

Figure 7.6   Proposal for minimum standard for the overall functional design.

Contents

- System architecture:
  (a) Program modules, functions, interfaces.
  (b) Data flows.
  (c) Data base definitions down to field level.
  (d) Hardware and basic software.
  (e) External technical interfaces.
- Production procedures.
- Plan for technical conversion.
- Evaluation of to what degree this design meets the requirements of the overall functional design.

Form

- A handbook (with index — could be computer based).

Functionality

- A working document for the system developers.

Figure 7.7 Proposal for minimum standard for the overall technical design.

The overall design has been divided into two parts. One part is called the overall functional design. The overall functional design describes the new user organization, including the new computer-based system. The other part is called the overall technical design. The overall technical design describes the new computer system. Accordingly one talks about technical conversion, which is the introduction of the new computer system into the existing technical environment, and functional conversion, which is the introduction of the new computer based system into the user organization.

Maintenance documentation

Maintaining the maintenance documentation is time consuming, but it makes it easier to maintain the system

As already mentioned, it is known from experience that the maintenance documentation is often neglected. It is a common belief that maintenance documentation consists of all the descriptions made during the system development process. This would be impractical, and the consequence is typically that only the program lists are kept up to date, and that they in reality constitute the only maintenance documentation. An important criterion for determining a minimum standard for maintenance documentation is that the benefit, in the form of easier maintenance of software, should be bigger than the cost of maintaining the documentation. Figure 7.8 suggests a minimum standard. This

As a minimum you need the following to maintain a system:

(a) **Survey descriptions**

These should show the correlation between jobs, files, and print lists.

(b) **Job descriptions**

These should contain technical information about jobs: name, parameters, prerequisites for running, program names. They refer to the program library.

(c) **Print lists**

There should be a file of all the types of print lists with examples.

(d) **Program library**

This should contain source code, job control language commands, data definitions, and code, which are copied into the programs.

(e) **Standards for using the program library**

These should include program name standard, principle for placing files, and principles for communication of changes to other programmers.

Figure 7.8 Proposal for minimum standard for maintenance documentation.

Exercise 7.2

Work out a standard

Work out a standard for overall design or for maintenance documentation.

- Find examples from your own or other projects.

- Describe contents and form in the examples and evaluate what is good and what is bad in relation to how the products are used.

- Compare with the proposals for minimum standards in Figures 7.6—7.8.

- Work out a standard on the basis of results of the above.

standard has been worked out and tested in cooperation with a maintenance group in a development organization.

7.3 Project management with baselines

Baselines support the mutual interaction between the three management functions

Baselines support the three subfunctions of project management: planning, evaluation, and regulation. Figure 7.9 illustrates these three subfunctions and their interaction.

Planning deals with future working practices and conditions of performing the project. Planning results in plans on various levels and of various courses of events, and in descriptions of the conditions which are a prerequisite of realizing the plans. Evaluation deals with the existing realities, with the process itself, and with the current plans. Evaluation leads to understanding the employed working practice and the current conditions of the project. Evaluation also leads to identification of errors and conflicts linked to the course of the project. It is important to

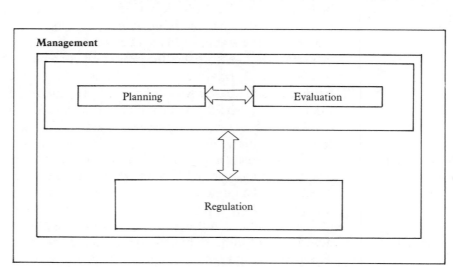

Figure 7.9   The process-oriented part of systems development.

evaluate the distance between current status and current plans. Regulation deals with the process as a whole. Regulation deals with the expectations, attitudes, and qualifications of the participants; with working practices in the project, and with the conditions characterizing the course of the project. Regulation results in changes in the process.

The principles of Chapter 3 stress that these activities should be performed concurrently. Evaluation and planning are mutually dependent and should therefore be performed concurrently in order to support each other (principle M1). Process-oriented reflection (planning and evaluation) and regulation of the process affect each other, and should therefore be performed concurrently (principle M2). Descriptions of baselines are important in the evaluation of the project. On the basis of a description of a baseline it is possible to evaluate the actual state of the project. It is possible to examine whether the baseline has been reached. The baseline also supports regulation of the project. Description of a baseline forms the basis of planning and changing working practices. A baseline which has been reached facilitates local planning and means that there is less need for intervention in the individual project participant's work routines.

Apart from describing the baselines, planning with baselines also includes the planning of activities to determine whether a baseline has been reached. These activities are called checkpoints. Maybe it would be better to call them check periods, because they include evaluation, planning, and repair activities which together will take some time. Planning with baselines also includes planning of activities which should be performed to ensure that the project moves forward from one baseline to the next. A phase comprises the activities which are performed between two baselines. The authors maintain that planning fundamentally should be formulated in terms of baselines. However, plans should also contain phases and activities. Figure 7.10 illustrates the relation between baselines, phases, and checkpoints.

Describe phases as well as baselines

It is far easier and more operational to determine whether a project has reached a described baseline than it is to determine a satisfactory conclusion of a number of activities as known from traditional division into phases. A good project plan should obviously include a description of both baselines and activities. A project is, however, traditionally described as a number of activities taking place in a number of phases. The expected project states at the start and at the end of the phases

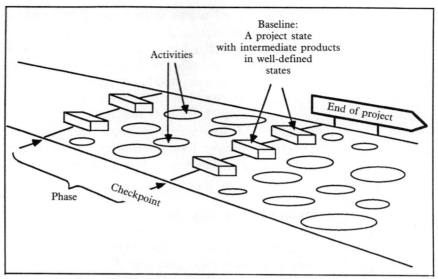

Figure 7.10 Planning the project in terms of phases with baselines and
checkpoints.

Baseline. Activities should be coordinated effectively.

are not described except in the form of, for instance, tables of contents of end-of-phase reports. Neither is it described how to evaluate whether the desired state has been reached. The transition from one phase to another thus takes place without an evaluation of the overall state of the project. This will impede a dynamic regulation of the course of the project and of the plans. The conclusion of phases tends to become formal goals which are only reached on paper. It is our principle that baselines and checkpoints are better than phases. Traditional division into phases confuses time and content, thus making a dynamic regulation of the course of events and of plans difficult (principle M5, Chapter 3).

Planning with baselines

Planning with baselines means that the planning of activities is improved through a better understanding of the expectations for the overall result of the activities. The temporal division in the project plan should be determined by which baselines are desirable and possible. What supports the users' understanding of the final product, and how can they influence the project? What can support the project participants' commitment and understanding of the project, both where the product and the process are concerned? Where in the project is it most important to ensure coordination? These are examples of questions which should be answered to find the desired baselines. At the same time they are questions which lead to considerations of which activities to perform, and what working practices to employ.

A project does not need to walk in step the whole time — on the contrary — this would be an impediment — but it is important to plan that the project closes up the ranks once in a while. Otherwise there is a risk that the project participants move too far away from each other. This might lead to the project suffocating in individual coordination efforts, or to the participants actually getting stuck and concentrating on details which are irrelevant for the progress in the project.

The number of baselines depends on the uncertainty in the project

Planning baselines very much depends on the degree of uncertainty in the project. If there is a high degree of uncertainty in and around the project, there should be many baselines at short intervals. If, for instance, there is uncertainty regarding requirements of the new computer system's functional properties, it would be a good idea to describe several baselines containing a number of descriptions and prototypes to illustrate various alternative design proposals. This would improve the basis for discussions and decisions, and diminish the degree of uncertainty. If, on the other hand, there is a high degree of certainty concerning the division of the final system into subsystems with well-defined interfaces, then it is possible to keep a longer distance between the checkpoints where the overall state of the project is evaluated. There might also be a need to describe baselines in the work with the individual subsystems. It might be convenient to establish a number of sub-projects each of which is responsible for its own subsystem.

System development projects usually include parallel development of different products and services. Basic software is designed on the basis of the functionality of the hardware. The application software is designed on the basis of the functionality of the basic software. Manuals are written on the basis of the functionality of the software, etc. If there are any changes in some of the prerequisites, it is important that these changes are communicated to the people who depend on them. Otherwise the result is a lot of wasted work, and the final product may prove useless because of poor adjustments to the changed prerequisites. Baselines are especially important in parallel development. Figure 7.11 describes a number of project situations where important baselines have been reached. The situations are characterized by the state of the primary product in the baseline. For each baseline, the project plan should also

---

- **Project start:**

  (a) The project charter and the first version of the project plan have been completed.
  (b) Preliminary version of overall design has been completed.

- **Overall design has been completed:**

  (a) Detailed design of sub-products has been completed.
  (b) Sub-products are ready for system test.
  (c) Services have been planned and tested.
  (d) The product is ready to go into production.
  (e) The product has been delivered and approved, most of the services have been rendered.

- **Project termination.**

Figure 7.11   Project situations where important baselines have been reached.

describe the overall state of the project, including prerequisites of the plan.

The most important baseline in a project is: overall design is completed. This is the objective of the initial analysis and design activities and the common frame of reference regarding the realization of the product. See an example of description of this baseline in Section 7.1.

Evaluating project states

Chapter 6 presented techniques for evaluating project situations. These techniques are especially applicable when evaluating whether a baseline has been reached. The status of the project should be evaluated in relation to a planned baseline. Criteria and procedures for evaluation form part of the description of the baseline. It is often a good idea to let one or more reviews enter into the evaluation process. The state of intermediate products should be evaluated, and the actual prerequisites of the future work should be compared with what is planned. Weaknesses in the actual project situation are often best elucidated by people outside the project. People external to the project should therefore always participate in the evaluation activities, in particular in reviews but also at other stages.

A delayed project may well have reached a baseline

A project state deviating from the planned baseline may act as a new baseline. A delayed project may have reached a baseline — only it is not the planned one. However, this requires that the actual baseline is described — intermediate products should be in well-defined states, and prerequisites in the plan should be met. Hence it is not enough to determine whether a baseline has been reached or not at some checkpoint. If the baseline has not been reached, the plan should be altered. And if you can see that the project has reached a well-defined project state, this may constitute a new baseline and form the basis of the plan rather than the earlier planned baseline. The project plan is then revised accordingly. Alternatively you may change the plan and add some activities and a new checkpoint to evaluate whether the original baseline has been reached.

In the example in Section 7.1 the planned intermediate state (overall design has been completed) was not reached, but the plans were not altered. The project group continued to work from a project state which was poorly described. This resulted in considerable delays and poor product quality. Unclear project states may easily result in problems delaying the project more than necessary. Baselines are frameworks for local planning. They are the most important factor in ensuring that the efforts of groups and individuals move the common project forward in the planned direction.

Plan with the fact that checkpoints take time and require resources

A fundamental requirement of planning with baselines is that time is set aside to bring the project up to the planned baseline after a checkpoint. The more activities like that are taken into consideration in the plan, the higher are the chances that the plan holds. Obviously this — along with many of the other recommendations in this chapter — may be hard to observe in practice because of time pressure, demands for quick solutions, etc. But it is our experience that project management with baselines is better than project management without them. The limits to what is possible under the given conditions can only be learned by crossing them once in a while. Use baselines in project management and plan with time and resources for both evaluation and regulation.

Exercise 7.3

Describe baselines and phases

Take your starting point in a project in which you have participated.

- Identify situations where the project completed a phase or a period.

- Evaluate the obtained intermediate states. Were they baselines? Why? What was lacking?

- How were the periods delimited in the plans? Did the project plan describe baselines or something like baselines? If not, could it have been done? Try to describe one or more possible baselines and compare them with actual descriptions in the plans.

7.4 Configuration management

Configuration management in systems development denotes the activities which, during development, maintenance, and further development, aim at ensuring that there always is a formally approved and accessible last version of the whole computer system and of different descriptions of the computer system. Configuration management includes management of product states and management of changes in product states.

Configuration management used to be linked to maintenance and further development during the operation of computer systems. Here it is absolutely necessary to know what version of the computer system is in production. However, configuration management is also important in systems development before production, among other things because of the size of the computer systems. The computer systems are divided into subsystems with important interfaces, and usually some parallel development takes place. Configuration management may, however, also be necessary where small programs are involved to safeguard against chaos and too strong dependency on individual persons.

There is plenty of literature describing configuration management as an independent theme, or describing it as a subject under quality assurance. It is also becoming increasingly more common that requirements of quality assurance, and thus configuration management, are stated in project contracts.

Baselines form the basis of configuration management

Baselines are important in configuration management. Descriptions of procedures for evaluating and approving for instance plans, design descriptions, code and manuals enter into the description of baselines. A verified baseline may then include an approved configuration. Configuration management is solely linked to management of the products in systems development. Services, for instance technical and functional conversion, do not enter into configuration management. The notion of baselines, on the other hand, embraces the whole project state — including the services.

A shared task

Configuration management is, as already mentioned, important both during development before production, and during maintenance and further development. Hence you should plan with configuration management activities all through the product life cycle. Configuration management makes a lot of demands on discipline, and the activity always requires that a number of formal procedures for evaluation and approval of products are carried out. This means that configuration management activities should not be restricted to the project group. The requirements of discipline and formal procedures indicate that configuration management is a common task linked to the development organization or the user organization as a whole. The literature is full of suggestions for how to carry out configuration management in practice, including organization, activities, tools, and procedures. Where organization of configuration management is concerned, the literature advises a library function in the project or in the development organization. Figure 7.12 lists the most important objectives of a library function. The library function in a project may be undertaken by a system developer or by a person who works with the administrative tasks of a project.

Need for flexibility as well as discipline

Configuration management during system development should be organized in such a way that the activities are carried out as close to the system developers as possible. Too much formalism and too many restrictions would impede flexibility in the development work. However, this must be balanced against lack of discipline, which is a danger if configuration management, on the basis of informal procedures, is left to the system developers themselves.

Here, as in other management functions, tools are important, though not enough in themselves. However, as configuration management is based on standards and formal procedures — as opposed to most other management activities — tools such as computer-based registration systems may prove decisive for the success of configuration management.

A library function should ensure that the following points are satisfied:

- The status of products is registered.
- Changes in products compared to the previous version are marked.
- Products in formally approved states are accessible.
- All deliveries of products are registered, including changes.

Figure 7.12   Objectives of a library function.

Further reading

The idea of baselines as a fundamental element in the project plan is based on the concept of baselines in the literature on management of system development projects — for instance Boehm (1981), Dunn and Ullman (1982). Among all the literature on configuration management we will mention Bersoff (1980) which contains a thorough discussion of the problem area.

8 Cooperation with the users

System developers need users

Most system developers have a professional pride — they wish to make good systems. A good system is good to work with. It forms part of a totality — the work process in the user organization. The system solves a number of relevant tasks, it contains only a few errors, it is well documented, and it is easy to maintain and easy to develop further. The question, however, is: how are good systems developed? The fundamental statement in this chapter is that the quality of the completed system depends on the relation between the system developers and the future users.

Section 8.1 looks at the various conditions for cooperation between system developers and users. Section 8.2 deals with how to describe systems in cooperation with users. Section 8.3 looks at some of the possibilities of experimental systems development. Section 8.4 argues that a successful cooperation between system developers and users requires the application of different perspectives during analysis and design. Finally Section 8.5 describes a technique for choosing forms of cooperation. The choice is based on the situation in which the project group finds itself.

8.1 Different conditions for cooperation

The knowledge of the users is a necessity. Firstly because it is the users' work which is going to be computer supported — they are the ones who will feel the consequences of the new system. Secondly because analysis and design activities contain a considerable element of problem setting. During analysis and design situations often arise where the task and also the procedure are unknown. To be able to formulate the task, it is necessary to know the (sometimes conflicting) needs of the users. Without this kind of knowledge the design easily becomes a matter of guesswork. It is a principle that technical oriented analysis and design may result in perfect solutions to the wrong problems. Qualified analysis and design require both technical, as well as organizational and social competence (principle P6, Chapter 3).

If you don't have a user, go find one

However, no system development projects are alike. Their relations to the user organization are very different. In Chapter 2 two extreme roles were formulated for the project group with respect to the user organization: those of supplier and consultant, respectively. One of the things characterizing the consultant is close contact to the users. The supplier, however, is often prevented from having any contact with the users, even though the success of the project still depends on whether an applicable system is made or not. That is why suppliers often try to find a user. They establish informal relations with a number of users, they employ an experienced user as a consultant, or they do something else to find a user. This is one of the reasons why suppliers and purchasers might find it profitable to establish development agreements. The purchaser gets a suitable system at a reasonable price, and the supplier avoids some of the costs of sending an incomplete standard product on the market.

Sometimes it looks as though there is no need for users. However, this is often because the system developers are users themselves. Well-known examples are development of text editors and other programming tools. It is no coincidence that many interesting experiments with interaction forms take place within programming environments.

Supplier. Lack of cooperation with users may result in perfect solutions to the wrong problems.

There are those who claim that system developers have no need for users. They may argue that system developers ought to base their work on the requirement specification alone. A requirement specification is another word for what we have called the overall functional design. Whatever the document is called, it still represents the users' expectations to the project's results, and can thus not be made without contact with the users. Neither can the overall functional design be made independently of the overall technical design and of the realization of the system. Practice indicates the following points:

- Users do not know, or at least are unable to formulate, precisely what it is they require.

- Even if the requirements are known, there will still be details which are not recognized until late in the project — details which entail changes in the design.

- Requirements change in the course of time because the user organization changes, or because new conflicts arise.

- Humans make mistakes.

- Part of the functional design is changed because other solutions prove less costly or superior.

All these uncertainties mean that analysis, design, and realization necessarily will affect one another, and it therefore pays to organize the project in a way that ensures that these activities are performed concurrently (see principles P1 and P2, Chapter 3).

Pushing it to extremes we could say that system developers have two possibilities if there are any uncertainties about the functional design; either they make more or less qualified guesses, or they examine what the requirements are. Unfortunately it is often the case that part of the design is based on guesswork. But what can you do when you are prevented from contacting the users — for instance when you are delivering software to a country far away — i.e. a clean-cut supplier situation? One possibility is to split up the delivery into a number of subdeliveries which may be negotiated at different points in time. In this way the contract can be adjusted in the course of the project, and in the extreme this will give both parties the opportunity to pull out of the contract. In any case you must be prepared to face relatively long installation and adaption periods when you deliver systems which have been developed without user contact.

Consultant. Direct cooperation between users and system developers is clearly to be preferred.

Even though the conditions may be very different, the relation to the users or to the user organization is still of decisive importance. Direct cooperation between the users and the system developers is clearly to be preferred. However, if this proves impossible the system developers must, in addition to the requirement specification, at least know the users' application situation (see principle P4, Chapter 3).

8.2 System description with or for the users

Cooperation between system developers and users may take many forms. The terms 'system description with the users' and 'system description for the users' will be used to discuss some fundamental differences in organizing cooperation in design and analysis.

*System
descriptions for
the users easily
degenerates to
advertising*

System description with the users is defined as an analysis and design activity contributing to the establishment of new knowledge, both where the users and where the system developers are concerned. System description for the users, on the other hand, is a communication activity where the system developers communicate analysis results or design proposals to the users.

System description *for* the users cannot be substituted for system description *with* the users. System developers and users find it hard to learn from each other if the system developers are the only ones playing an active role. Apart from that there is a tendency that system description for the users degenerates to something resembling advertisements — descriptions with the objective of selling the system. This will not encourage the users' willingness and ability to comment on the proposals, and the system developers' need for criticism and knowledge of the application situation will not be satisfied.

However, establishing a good system description with the users is not easy, since system developers cannot expect the users to be able or willing to play an active role in a traditionally organized project where technical questions are in focus. If the users are to play an active role, the technical problems must always be seen in relation to the users' work and organization. Another important issue is that the discussions are made concrete. If you wish to make system descriptions with the users, working practices must be adapted accordingly. These two principles are elaborated in the following and Figure 8.1 summarizes the main points involved in creating a system description with the users.

*Bring in
different kinds
of knowledge*

First you must alternate between general descriptions of the users' work and their organization on one hand, and the special descriptions of the computer system and its interaction with the users and their work on the other hand. These two types of description must be undertaken concurrently to support each other. Understanding the users' work and organization will make it possible to evaluate the importance of a given computer application. Understanding a concrete application will help to decide what aspects of the users' work are important to get to know. Our principle is that qualified analysis and design requires technical as well as organizational and social competence (principle P6, Chapter 3). In practice the project should be organized in a way that ensures that different kinds of knowledge are brought into it, and in a way that ensures interaction between different viewpoints. If you start with the organizational and work routine aspects alone, it will become more or less impossible to delimit the relevant aspects. If, on the other hand,

System description with users is an analysis and design activity in which the following hold:

- Both users and system developers gain new knowledge.

- Technical questions are always seen in relation to the users' work and the organization in which the technology is going to be applied.

- There is an interaction between general descriptions of the users' work and special descriptions of the computer system and the latter's relation to the users' work.

- Concrete visions of the new system and its consequences for the users' work situation are created.

Figure 8.1   Characteristics of system description with the users.

you start with a technical viewpoint, it will prove difficult to maintain the attention of the users, and it will become more or less impossible to evaluate the quality of the descriptions and proposals. Section 8.4 looks at the application of several perspectives in a system development project.

Be concrete and   Secondly you must make sure that the discussions are held on a
still imaginative   concrete level. The analysis and design activities in traditional projects are often characterized by abstract discussions. However, both the users and the system developers need to be able to imagine the new system and its interaction with the users' work. If the users do not have a clear idea of the new system, they will find it almost impossible to participate in and contribute to the design discussions. But what can be done in practice? One possibility is to develop prototypes. We return to that in Section 8.3. Another possibility is to visit other companies to look at similar systems. Visits like that will create a shared and concrete basis on which the users and system developers can communicate about the system they are developing. It is a principle that there is a need for interaction between product-oriented reflection (analysis and design) and realization of products and services (principle P2, Chapter 3). If you start with the reflection activities alone, you will make it hard for those participants who are not used to abstract reasoning and description, and there is a risk that users and system developers will talk at cross-purposes without realizing it. If, on the other hand, you rush into developing prototypes or visiting other companies, you will risk losing sight of the actual problems because imagination is limited at an early stage by the available possibilities.

8.3 Experimental systems development

System developers often find that their systems are being criticized when they are completed, and feel that such criticism could have been put forward when the design proposals were presented. It is, however, hard to get a mental picture of the future system on the basis of descriptions on a piece of paper. Experimental systems development — or prototyping — is an attempt at doing something about this. Experimental systems development may be practised in many ways. However, systems all have in common that an early test version of the product is developed.

Prototypes are used in many industries. In the motor industry, for instance, a prototype is the first (not mass-produced) specimen of an industrial product. Such prototypes are faithful copies of the finished product. They are often very costly. In architecture and town planning — where single-unit production predominates — models are often produced on a reduced scale. Prototypes of this kind make it easier for others to understand the design proposal. The idea behind experimental systems development is based on experience from these other fields. According to our theory experimental systems development supports the principle that product-oriented reflection (analysis and design) should be performed concurrently with realization (principle P2, Chapter 3). However, there are, as already mentioned, many different forms of experimental systems development.

What is the objective of the experiment?

First, experiments are carried out for different reasons. One objective may be to develop visions of the future system. Another may be to develop the finished product.

Some experiments aim at formulating better visions of the new system. Experimenting with prototypes results in a clearer and more understandable vision. This vision can be realized later in a more conventional manner. Prototypes like that will normally be difficult or impossible to use again in the finished product. The main focus in such experiments is on developing the functional design.

Other experiments aim at working out a good technical design of the final product. The computer system is developed and modified in interplay with a series of experiments. The overall functional design is altered to only a moderate degree. In experiments of this type it is important that parts of the prototype can be reused in the finished production system. Such experiments require a lot of applied programming tools.

What does the experiment embrace?

Secondly, the extent to which the experiment goes towards the final system varies a great deal in the actual application situation. The fundamental idea behind experimental systems development is to create an interplay between notions and ideas linked to the visions, and the concrete experiences resulting from realizing and testing a version of the finished product. The experiment will usually deal with a system which will correspond to the final system only on some points. Two basic kinds of experiment can be distinguished:

- The system is a complete realization of selected parts of the functional design. This type of experiment may be called vertical prototyping. An experiment may, for instance, contain a selected part of a man— machine interface where every detail is included, for instance data base, error handling, and display screens.

- The system facilitates a demonstration of all the aspects of the functional design, but the parts are not realized in every detail. This type of experiment may be called horizontal prototyping. The experiment may, for instance, aim at determining the layout of the displays. The prototype can thus be demonstrated — without including any real data or error situations.

The extent of the experiment depends on the environments in which the prototype is being tested. The test may take place in the development organization, in simulated user environments, or in the actual use situation.

How do we evaluate?

Thirdly, the experiments may be organized differently in relation to the evaluation or analysis of the prototype. Different people may undertake the evaluations: the system developers themselves, selected user representatives, or all the users. The evaluation may also be organized in many different ways. At one extreme the activity may take place as an informal test. At the other extreme the analysis may be organized as a systematic study on the basis of previously determined questions. It is in any case important to evaluate the prototype to ensure the intended effect in the form of new design and analysis activities.

Experimental systems development, with the purpose of formalizing visions, makes it possible to practise systems description with the users. By applying prototypes the users get a true opportunity to participate in the formulation of the project's goals. However, this requires that the system developers have the possibility to — and are willing to — construct a number of prototypes with the sole objective of facilitating a discussion of the users' problems and needs. This is one reason why easy and fast prototypes are an advantage. The idea is that testing the various possibilities provokes the users to formulate their opinions.

Problems

Experimental systems development is not without its problems and pitfalls. Experiments support the systems development process seen as a process of cognition. There is lots of room for visions and imaginative design proposals. It may, however, be difficult to keep the wishes and visions on a realistic level. Experimental systems development contains the contradiction of flying high with both feet firmly on the ground (principle P5, Chapter 3).

Experiments require active management

Experimental processes are difficult to manage. There must be enough time to carry out the experiments, but time must also be set aside to finish a production system. These two considerations must be balanced against each other, and weighing this balance requires insight into the course of the experiments and into the future extent of the realization work. Here, as in all other systems development work, it is important to create a link between performance and management. However, it may be difficult to get insight into the experimental process, and it may be impossible to determine the progress of the experiment.

Developing a prototype may also invite short-term cost savings. The original objective of the experiment may well be to generate good ideas for the functional design before the actual development of the system is initiated. However, there is a risk that financial aspects and strict time schedules entail that the prototype — which was supposed to be discarded — is put into operation anyway. A situation like that will often give the users a lot of problems because prototypes do not exhibit the operational stability to be expected from a production system.

Finally prototypes may create tunnel vision. An early prototype may lead to the fact that the users', as well as the system developers', attention is concentrated on the prototype. Other alternative possibilities are overlooked. The result of the process may be applicable — but without being all that relevant as regards the real problem. In other words, it is dangerous to experiment with a prototype before you know the user organization and its needs.

Tools

One of the requirements surfacing in connection with experimental systems development is the need for efficient systems development tools. The tools are important elements in testing the various ideas quickly enough. New tools do, however, have their pros and cons, and new tools are not always the solution to every problem.

A project postponed the realization of the print-out part of a system until a report generator could be installed. When the report generator finally arrived a year after it was supposed to, several modules turned out too inefficient. The modules had to be re-coded in a traditional programming language.

In another case a large project was interrupted while an integrated development tool with its own data-base system was being installed. When the tool had been installed, it turned out that the existing systems could not use the new data-base system. All the company's computer applications had to be changed.

However, efficient tools are obviously important. A large development organization did not have the capacity to realize even the simplest requirements. The installation of a fourth-generation tool meant that changes, which had been postponed indefinitely, could be implemented within a week.

Exercise 8.1

Arrange an experiment

Discuss the arrangement of an experiment — either in relation to a project which has just been concluded, or in relation to a project which is about to start up.

- What is the objective of the experiment?
- How far should the experiment go towards the real-life host organization?
- How will you arrange evaluation of the prototype?
- How does the experiment affect the management activities in the project?
- Which development tools would support the experiment?

8.4 Use of different perspectives

Applying a method implies the use of some specific perspective

It does make a difference how system developers describe and understand the user organization. Not all aspects are equally relevant. There are different ways in which to understand an organization. Applying one specific systems development method implies that the system developer uses some specific perspective. The method's description tools are only able to describe certain aspects of the user organization. The method's prescriptions of how the work should be done, for instance the method's techniques, will also affect the applied perspective. The method may, for instance, recommend that you talk with certain user groups and not with others.

The system developer's perspective is important on several levels. On an overall level the relations between groups and individuals can be seen in different ways. There will always be some signs of relatively harmonious relations, and other signs of the opposite. Some organizations and situations are naturally more characterized by conflicts than others. At the same time the same — or apparently the same — phenomenon is interpreted in different ways. In a conflict-perspective the conflict-ridden episode may be interpreted as an expression of a more fundamental, permanent conflict. In a harmony-perspective the same episode may be interpreted as a mistake or a communication problem. It is important to pay attention to the potential conflicts in an organization. Systems development entails changes which may provoke old, concealed conflicts.

There are several perspectives on systems development and computer applications as a whole. In a media perspective, computer systems are compared to the telephone, the postal service, and the newspapers. This seems an obvious perspective on applications like electronic mail and electronic bulletin boards, but an office information system may also be seen as a medium. The ideal in this perspective is to create efficient and transparent communication between the involved users. In a tool perspective, on the other hand, the computer system is seen as the working tool. The ideal in this perspective is a computer system which can meet the requirements of the working process. When one uses a hammer, attention is on the nail — not the hammer. A good computer system should enable the user to concentrate on what he or she is working on (a document, an invoice, a newspaper page, a design). Depending on whether the system developers take on one or the other perspective, they focus on different things, and different concepts of quality of product and services will surface.

Perspective: standpoint, selection, and interpretation

A perspective is something a person applies when he or she works with a phenomenon. A perspective has three important characteristics. First, the perspective is linked to the standpoint of the person who describes the phenomenon. Secondly, the application of the perspective results in a specific selection of properties in the phenomenon in question. Thirdly, these selected properties are interpreted in some specific way. Figure 8.2 illustrates two relevant perspectives on the users' work.

Perspectives are primarily distinguished by different standpoints. Differences in selection can be illustrated by looking at descriptions of material and information flows, respectively. The person doing the describing may look at the same work situation, but depending on whether he or she applies one or the other perspective, he or she will

select different properties of the work situation. Difference in interpretation is often linked to the describing person's personal characteristics. Two people describing the same phenomenon may look at it and select the same properties. The result may still turn out to be different because their attitudes, values, and fundamental assumptions are different.

It is important that system developers are aware of the perspective they are applying. It is impossible fully to understand the user organization. It is also impossible fully to understand how the users see their work. To avoid unnecessary misunderstandings or faulty designs, the system developer must know the limitations and strengths of his or her understanding of the user organization. This will facilitate new analysis, should this prove necessary. Knowing the limits of one's understanding is also an important prerequisite of being able to organize working practices sensibly.

In some cases disagreement may arise between different parties

A given work situation may be seen either in a bird's-eye perspective or in a man's-eye perspective.

Bird's-eye perspective

In a bird's-eye perspective the work situation is typically seen from above, and this perspective represents the executive's or the manager's way of seeing the work. Attention is paid to the overall purpose of the work.

The advantages of this perspective are linked to the overall, general understanding which is obtained. An understanding like that is often a prerequisite of being able to construct a computer system which is going to be used by more than one person. This perspective is also a prerequisite of being able to plan organizational innovations.

Man's-eye perspective

In a man's-eye perspective the work situation is typically seen from within, and this perspective represents the end-user's way of seeing the work. It is the total work situation of the individual which forms the basis of understanding the work.

The advantage of this perspective is that it gives an understanding of variations and differences in the work. This understanding is a prerequisite for a cooperation with a person in a given work situation.

Figure 8.2   Bird's-eye and man's-eye perspective on a work situation.

because they have different perspectives. If the disagreement can be traced back to different standpoints or difference in selection, the disagreement can be overcome if the involved parties get together and explain and describe how they see the situation. If, on the other hand, the disagreement is due to difference in interpretation, it may prove impossible to reach any agreement. Different interpretations are often linked to different interests or different fundamental assumptions. In cases like that compromise is the only way out.

Use different perspectives   There will always be several relevant perspectives on the same phenomenon. When developing office systems it is a good idea to see the system as a tool and as a medium for the office workers. It may prove expedient to apply a certain systems development method and thus the perspective of this method. System developers should also try to see the situation, the work, and the changes, from the users' point of view. This can be done by applying a bird's-eye perspective and various man's-eye perspectives. Finally it might be relevant to take on a conflict perspective: will the new system shift the power structure in the organization or result in other conflicts? The advantage of applying all these perspectives is that a varied understanding, and thus a better basis on which to make the design, is achieved. The system developer will, however, never be able to share a user's perspective fully, since users, as opposed to system developers, form part of, and do not look at, their own working situation.

There are techniques which are suitable for supporting the application of several perspectives. One possibility is to use different metaphors. To use a metaphor is to apply the image of something well-known when trying to understand a related, not yet fully understood phenomenon. A designer uses metaphors when he makes a design analogous to something he has designed earlier. In certain kinds of interactive word processing, for instance, interaction has been developed which successfully could be transferred to other types of computer applications. The tool perspective and the medium perspective may be applied outside their natural field. This is how a tool and a medium metaphor is created. Experiments with prototypes may help system developers to take on other perspectives. By developing prototypes with the users the system developers are forced to consider how it would be to work with the system. This makes it easier for them to identify with the users' work situation.

Exercise 8.2

Characterize your perspective on the user organization

Try to characterize your own perspective on the user organization. What is your standpoint? What aspects of the user organization do you see as the most important ones? Which aspects do you ignore? How do you interpret those aspects of the user organization that you know? What is the importance of the methods employed for your perspective?

Exercise 8.3

Create metaphors of systems

Try to see the system you are working on as a tool for the users, as a medium, as an information system.

Try to create ideas for other metaphors.

The point of this section can be summarized as the principle that qualified analysis and design requires different perspectives to be applied. The techniques and tools, as well as the way in which the process is organized, should vary according to the situation (principle P7, Chapter 3). Chapter 9 will elaborate on this point.

8.5 Choice of form of cooperation

One of the key messages in this book is that the working practices — and especially cooperation with the users — should be organized on the basis of the project situation. The first opportunity of planning the project's working practices presents itself when the project is established, but it is important to keep adapting the working practices to the current situation all through the project. A prerequisite of current adaptation is that the project situation is evaluated regularly. An evaluation like that is best based on experience from earlier projects. That is why it is important that the system developers sum up their experiences — the bad as well as the good ones — and communicate these experiences to the rest of the development organization.

There are some general concepts and techniques for evaluating project situations. Chapter 2 describes three types of situations: routine situations, problem-solving situations, and problem-setting situations. These three types of situations call for completely different working practices. The temptation to handle any situation as a routine situation is obvious: it would save many discussions. The only problem is that you risk overlooking problematic or fuzzy aspects of the situation. This could prove costly in the long run.

Another equivalent way to evaluate situations is to examine task uncertainty. A high degree of uncertainty requires a high degree of flexibility, among other things limited division of work. A low degree of uncertainty corresponds to routine tasks. Here there is less need for intervening and changing working practices, and more specialized working practices can be applied successfully.

Different forms of cooperation

How do we determine the system's characteristics?

There are many forms of cooperation with the users. They all focus on determining the characteristics of the future system. Four fundamentally different forms of cooperation will be discussed, and it will be illustrated how to choose from among them by taking a starting point in the project situation.

Firstly, you can stick to talking with the users. These conversations may be more or less structured: interviews, group discussions, or brainstorming. This type of cooperation generally requires that the users enter into the discussions with a clear idea of what it is they want. This working practice is inexpensive — at least in the short run.

Secondly, you can base the cooperation on analysis of a known system. One alternative would be to analyse a similar system in another organization, another would be to analyse a standard system. Requirements of the new computer system should be formulated on the basis of the analysed system. This working practice requires that the functionality of the future system is known, and that this functionality does not deviate too much from the analysed system. The working practice does, however, help the users to formulate what it is they want.

Thirdly, you can carry out a systematic analysis of the users' work situation and of different design proposals. This working practice facilitates new ways of thinking both where the possible forms of organization, and the possible applications of the computer, are concerned. The working practice is extensive and requires that the participants are able to make abstractions. Many methods prescribing this working practice are based on the ideal of the rational systems development process.

The fourth and last form of cooperation we will discuss here is experimental systems development. This working practice makes it possible to handle the uncertainties concerning the properties of the new system. The working practice does not make the same demands on the participants' ability to make abstractions, but it does make great demands of the development tools. Experimental systems development encourages new ways of thinking where the possible applications of the new system are concerned.

These four forms of cooperation should be seen as paradigms which should be determined in more detail in the given situation, and which in all probability should be supplemented with elements from other working practices.

A technique for choosing forms of cooperation

The following will discuss a technique for choosing forms of cooperation. The technique is suitable for choosing from among one of the four above-mentioned forms of cooperation. The technique is based on an analysis of the task uncertainty by analysing the four types of prerequisites of the project, for instance:

- The object area in the user organization.
- The new computer system.
- The users' qualifications and experience.
- The system developers' qualifications and experience.

The degree of uncertainty in the project situation is determined on the basis of an analysis of these four areas. Depending on the degree of uncertainty, project participants choose the primary form of cooperation for the project. The participants may also choose a supplementary, secondary form of cooperation. The technique has four steps (see Figure 8.3).

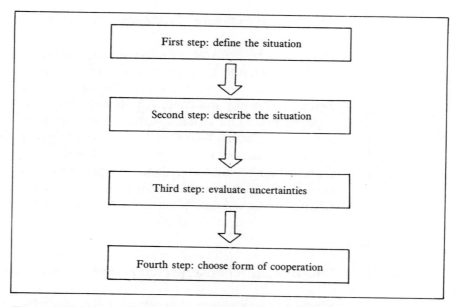

Figure 8.3 The four steps in the technique for choosing forms of cooperation when determining the properties of the future system.

First step: define the situation

The situation is defined and delimited by answering the following questions:

- What is the object area of the project?
- What kind of system is going to be developed?
- Who are the users of the new system?
- Who are the system developers?

The answers to these questions should be short and on an overall level.

Second step: describe the situation

The situation should be described by answering a number of questions about the four areas of analysis which were defined in the first step. These questions are elaborated in Figure 8.4. Even though it might seem rather artificial, the technique requires that you choose one, and only one of the indicated answers.

Third step: evaluate the degree of uncertainty

The results from the second step are now applied to evaluate the degree of uncertainty in three areas: existence and stability of the requirements of the system, ability of the users to formulate requirements of the system, and finally ability of the system developers to elicit and evaluate requirements. This is not a matter of summing up, but a qualitative evaluation of which factors affect the uncertainty in the three areas in the given situation. On the basis of this evaluation you determine the degree of uncertainty to be high, average, or low. Positive answers in the second step will contribute to a low degree of uncertainty. In Figure 8.5 the questions from the second step are arranged according to which of the three areas they affect.

Fourth step: choose primary form of cooperation

Finally the total degree of uncertainty is evaluated — again a qualitative consideration. The primary, and sometimes also a secondary form of

	No	Maybe	Yes
Object area:			
• Is there a usable description of the object area?	☐	☐	☐
• Is the object area characterized by stability?	☐	☐	☐
• Are there any set procedures?	☐	☐	☐
• Is the applied information stable?	☐	☐	☐
Computer system:			
• Is the computer system only applied on lower levels in the organization?	☐	☐	☐
• Is the system easy to understand?	☐	☐	☐
The users:			
• Is the user group homogeneous?	☐	☐	☐
• Do the users have a capacity for abstraction?	☐	☐	☐
• Do the users have any experience with the tasks in the object area?	☐	☐	☐
• Do the users have any experience with equivalent computer systems?	☐	☐	☐
• Do the users have any experience with systems development?	☐	☐	☐
The system developers:			
• Do the system developers have any knowledge of the tasks in the object area?	☐	☐	☐
• Do the system developers have any experience with development of equivalent systems?	☐	☐	☐
• Do the system developers have experience with analysis and design?	☐	☐	☐

Figure 8.4 Describe the situation (second step).

The existence and stability of requirements to the system:

- Is there a usable description of the object area?
- Is the object area characterized by stability, especially as regards procedures and information?
- Is the computer system easy to understand?
- Is the user group homogeneous?

Uncertainty	High	Average	Low

Ability of users to formulate requirements:

- Is the system only used on lower levels in the organization?
- If the object area characterized by stability, especially as regards procedures and information?
- Is the computer system easy to understand?
- Is the user group homogeneous?
- Do the users have a capacity for abstraction?
- Do the users have any experience with similar computer systems?
- Do the users have any experience with systems development?

Uncertainty	High	Average	Low

Ability of system developers to elicit and evaluate requirements:

- Is the computer system easy to understand?
- Do the system developers have any analysis and design experience?
- Do the system developers know the tasks in the object area?

Uncertainty	High	Average	Low

Figure 8.5 Evaluate the degree of uncertainty (third step).

cooperation is chosen on the basis of this evaluation (see Figure 8.6). After this the working practice is determined in more detail.

On first sight this technique may seem almost naive. Maybe it is unreasonable to summarize the evaluation of the situation in a one-dimensional uncertainty measurement. However, an argument in defence of this technique is that the evaluations are qualitative. Experience with the technique also indicates that the discipline which the technique forces on the evaluation process gives a thorough understanding of the situation. The technique is furthermore only a technique for choice of overall form of cooperation. The concrete way

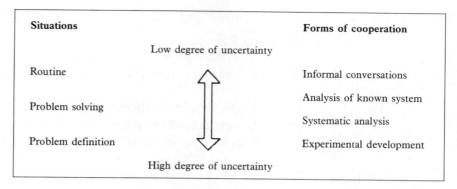

Figure 8.6   The relation between situations, uncertainty and forms of cooperation.

to organize the work process should take detailed evaluations of the degree of uncertainty into consideration. It is especially important to distinguish between the users' uncertainty and the system developers' uncertainty when choosing the form of cooperation between users and systems developers.

How applicable is a generally formulated technique like this? Well, the idea behind the technique is simple — and the individual project or development organization is free to adapt the technique to the areas which are considered important, and to the possible types of cooperation. Figure 8.7 illustrates how a supplier organization — on the basis of this technique — has worked out its own list of parameters to be considered when planning the working practice in a project.

Exercise 8.4

Choose form of cooperation

Choose a project which has been completed, or formulate a known situation (corresponding to the first step in the technique for choice of form of cooperation).

Apply the technique on the basis of this. Which form of cooperation would you give first priority? Second priority? What are the arguments for this? How does this correspond with experience and expectations?

Exercise 8.5

Work out a technique for choosing form of cooperation

Draw up a technique for choosing form of cooperation. Take your starting point in the properties of the new system and adapt them to your own organization (see Figure 8.7).

The task

- Has the task been solved manually in the organization?
- Is the task solved by an existing computer system?
- Are we dealing with new development or with modification?
- What is the degree of parallel development?
- Is the complexity of the system high?
- Are there any standards to be followed?
- What is the size if the project in man-hours?

The user organization

- Has the user organization received products from us before?
- Does the user organization have any experience with this type of project?
- What degree of commitment can we expect from the user organization?
- What is the decision capability in the user organization?
- What are the possibilities for communication with those who take over the system?
- Is there any possibility of getting an insight into the work routines in the user organization?

The development organization

- Is the assignment known in the organization?
- Is the assignment known in the project group?
- What does the project group know abut the hardware and the software?
- What is the profile of the project group as regards:
  (a) Qualifications?
  (b) Social interaction?
  (c) Available time?

The form of the descriptions

- To what degree are the requirements to the system determined?
- Who is the target audience of the descriptions?
- Are there any specific standards to be followed?
- How is quality given priority compared with the planned resources?

Figure 8.7   A company supplying computer systems has formulated these parameters to be taken into consideratioin when choosing the form of cooperation.

Further reading

System description with the users is described in more detail, in Munk-Madsen (1978). Experimental systems development has been discussed by many authors of systems development literature. Budde (1984) contains an extensive collection of articles on the subject. Our presentation of the perspective concept is inspired by Nygaard and Sørgaard (1985), Andersen and Kjær (1984), and Ehn and Sandberg (1979). The technique for choosing forms of cooperation is based on Davis (1982).

9 Description — vary working practices and perspective

Analysis and design require intuition, imagination, and common sense

System
developers
understand
more than they
are able to
describe

The fundamental objective of systems development is to produce a computer system and to change the user organization. However, the changes are obtained in an interaction with the reflective activities analysis and design, and this chapter will focus on these activities. A closer look will be taken at description forms and they will be discussed in relation to the description processes as well as to the resulting products: the descriptions. The main focus will be on descriptions as being the most characteristic common property of analysis and design. It is, however, important to remember that the understanding which the participants achieve during the analysis and design activities is always more comprehensive and varied than what will be expressed in the descriptions. That is why analysis and design are called reflective activities.

Chapter 8 also dealt with analysis and design. But that chapter concentrated on the problems linked to cooperation between users and system developers. Chapter 9, however, will look at descriptions of systems and working processes as a discipline in itself. The overall principle is that it is impossible to perform qualified analysis and design strictly according to given guidelines. The important requirements are experience, intuition, imagination, and reflection (principle P3, Chapter 3). The situations surfacing during analysis and design are not always routine situations. You will often find it unclear which working practice is the most suitable. At other times you will even find it unclear what it is you are going to describe, or why it should be described. The overall recommendation is therefore to vary your working practice as well as your perspective during the description work.

Section 9.1 takes a closer look at the analysis and design activities. Section 9.2 characterizes the various processes which are typical of description work. The question is addressed of whether the commonly accepted recommendation to work top-down makes any sense at all. Section 9.3 takes a closer look at some of the various ways of forming and applying concepts in the description work. Section 9.4 finally lists the various types of working practices and perspectives you can apply during analysis and design.

9.1 Analysis and design

As already mentioned in Chapter 3, the performance of systems development, the product-oriented part, consists of the reflective

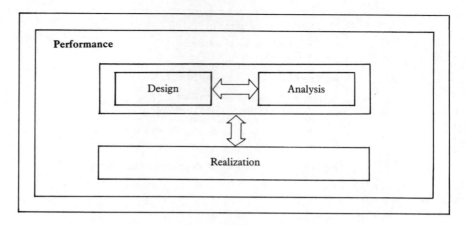

Figure 9.1   The product-oriented part of systems development.

functions, analysis and design, as well as of the innovative function, realization (see Figure 9.1).

Descriptions and description processes play an important part in the design and analysis activities. This section will first take a look at analysis and design separately, and afterwards it will look at their interrelations. Finally the consequences of the different objectives and needs linked to the description work will be discussed.

Analysis to understand

The analysis function is directed at the present reality: at the user organization, the technical possibilities, and at the available design proposals. The analysis function results in an understanding of the user organization, of the technical possibilities, and of the design proposals. The analysis identifies the areas in the user organization and the new system requiring design reflections.

The resulting descriptions may be employed to maintain the understanding and insight which has been achieved. The participants in analysis have, however — as already mentioned — always achieved a more comprehensive understanding than it will be possible to describe. They may employ the descriptions as an entry to remind them of what they have learned and agreed upon. The descriptions may also be employed to disseminate the analysis results to others who have not participated in the analysis process. The descriptions may furthermore act as a basis for making decisions and for the design activities. These points are summarized in Figure 9.2.

The description process:

- To achieve understanding.
- Communication.

The descriptions:

- To maintain understanding.
- To communicate understanding.
- To form basis for design.
- To form basis for making decisions.

Figure 9.2   Objectives of descriptions in analysis.

Examples of analysis activities are as follows:

- Describing working processes.
- Describing data flows.
- Interviewing users about their current practices.
- Visiting other companies to study similar systems.
- Describing technical possibilities.
- Evaluating design proposals.

Analysis
requires
empathy

Some of the activities are documented in separate descriptions. Other activities contribute to arguments in the design documents.

If the project group acts as suppliers, they are rarely expected to analyse the user organization. But even if the project group undertakes this analysis, it is still uncertain whether they achieve real understanding of the work in the user organization. The work content may be difficult to understand and describe. The current organization may be a result of many years of experience where the work tasks are concerned — so many years that no one knows any more why the work was organized the way it was.

The analysis of the technical aspects should reveal the possibilities and limitations of the current technology. There may already be a computer system solving some of the tasks of the new system. Maybe the new system is expected to take over some of the old system's functions, or it is expected to work together with the old system. If the hardware of the new system is already given, the properties of this hardware should be examined. If the choice of hardware is open, the hardware market should be investigated.

Design to change

Design is directed towards the future technical and organizational possibilities. Design embraces the formulation of one or more visions of possible innovations in the user organization. Design also embraces the clarification of these visions in the form of design proposals. Design results in descriptions of programs, computer systems, and working processes. (See Figure 9.3.)

Design is a creative activity   Design is a question of making proposals for how the future computer-based system should look. The problem is seldom well defined beforehand, and the formulation of the problem will change along the way. Design is therefore rarely routine work, and design also often contains more than problem solving. Design is a creative activity requiring experience, intuition, knowledge, and common sense.

Different groups have different visions of possible changes. It is important to formulate and discuss these visions so that possibilities, problems, and disagreements come out into the open. Design is not

The description process:

- To create visions.
- Communication.
- To clarify visions.

The descriptions:

- To maintain visions.
- To communicate visions.
- To form basis for negotiations.
- To maintain compromises.
- To form basis for making decisions.
- To form basis for realization.

Figure 9.3 Objectives of descriptions in design.

only a question of finding the solution to a given problem, but rather a question of investigating the possibilities for acceptable and feasible solutions.

Examples of design activities are as follows:

- Working out tenders.
- Brainstorming.
- Determining system architecture.
- Determining working processes.

Examples of descriptions are as follows:

- Overall functional design.
- Overall technical design.
- Descriptions of the user interface.
- Structured data descriptions.
- Decomposition into modules.
- Program outlines.
- User manuals.

There are conflicts between the different objectives and needs linked to the description work. One description cannot capture everything.

Analysis and design are connected

Analysis and design should be performed concurrently

Analysis and design are two different functions that can be thought of and related to as separate phenomena. However, this does not mean that analysis and design in practice can or should be temporally separated. Who has not had design ideas during analysis? Who has not

Analysis is the starting point of design.

It is the objective of the design that delimits the area of analysis.

Design ideas are conceived during analysis.

Design proposals should also be subjected to analysis.

Figure 9.4   Analysis and design should be performed concurrently.

been in a situation where the design work has revealed need for new analysis activities? Analysis and design are mutually dependent, and should therefore be performed concurrently (principle P1, Chapter 3). Figure 9.4 presents some arguments which will be elaborated in the following.

Analysis is the starting point of design. The designer should be thoroughly acquainted with the user organization and the problems forming the basis of the project. Even if the project is based on a precisely formulated product contract, it will be impossible to avoid situations where the designer will have to choose between alternatives. A good understanding of the user organization is a prerequisite of making the right decision. It is a principle that good design is a question of flying high — and keeping both feet firmly on the ground. It is important to create new visions and unconventional solutions, but it must be possible to introduce them in the organization (principle P5, Chapter 3).

It is the objective of the design that delimits the area of analysis. Reality — the user organization — may be looked upon from many different angles. Try to think of your local bank. What are the relevant aspects of this bank in relation to a system development project? Many aspects may be irrelevant irrespective of what kind of future system is to be developed: the geographical location of the bank, or the number of steps leading up to the main entrance. It is more difficult to determine the relevant aspects. There is in any case a big difference between what is relevant in relation to teller machines, and what is relevant in relation to computer systems for handling special loans for real estate construction. A design — a vision of innovations — is a prerequisite of being able to work efficiently with analysis. Without this vision it would be impossible to determine what aspects of the user organization it is relevant to include.

Design ideas are conceived during analysis. While discussing errors and inexpediencies, both the users and the system developers often get ideas of how the problems could be solved with the aid of computer technology. Many methods prescribe that analysis should be kept clean, and that you forget all design ideas at this point in time. But why not accept the way our imaginations work — and make use of this fact? Design ideas can be maintained systematically, even if the main objective of the work is analysis. Ideas and impressions may, for instance, be written down in a diary.

Design proposals should also be analysed. Technical and organizational changes are planned during the design activities. The ideas should be evaluated in relation to the user organization and in relation to the technical conditions of the project. It might turn out that the design idea is impossible to implement because of the limited technical possibilities. In this way you learn something new about the technical conditions. It may also turn out — especially if the users participate in the design discussions — that the task you are about to automate is sometimes carried out in quite a different way than suggested in the design. An analysis of a design proposal often brings forward new knowledge about the user organization.

Because analysis and design are interdependent in the way described above, it is important for the quality of the product that analysis and design activities are performed concurrently. In reality there will always be a certain amount of parallelism and interaction between design and analysis — irrespective of plans and intentions. In the beginning of a project, however, analysis will usually play the most dominant role. During the course of the project the weight will slowly shift from analysis over to design. The main direction of movement in systems development is illustrated in Figure 9.5. It is also important not to separate analysis and design organizationally. The overall understanding obtained during analysis cannot be disseminated in descriptions. It is therefore clearly preferable that the same people participate in the analysis, design and realization activities.

Conflicts between different objectives

Is the objective to maintain understanding, to achieve understanding, or to support construction?

You may emphasize different objectives and needs in the description work, for instance the knowledge represented in the descriptions. This is often the case if the descriptions are important to the communication process in the project. Descriptions should always be evaluated in relation to their applicability in various forms of communication:

- Internally in the project group.
- Between different user groups.

> ## Exercise 9.1
>
> **Evaluate analysis and design activities**
>
> Map the analysis and design activities in your last project and make a list of the project's descriptions.
>
> Characterize the various descriptions and discuss how they were connected.
>
> What was the correlation between the analysis and design work?
>
> Why was the project organized the way it was? Could it have been done differently?

- Between the project group and different user groups.
- Between the project group and computer operations.
- Between the project group and the maintenance group.
- Between the project group and the steering committee.

Different aspects are of interest to different groups.

The descriptions may also be seen as tools in the analysis and design process. They may support the process by reminding the participants of important aspects. They may also be suitable as future references for those who made the descriptions. In the latter case it is not the dissemination value of the descriptions which is emphasized: the descriptions are designed to support the understanding of the people who worked out the descriptions.

Finally the descriptions may serve as a basis for realizing the computer-based system. This will require that the descriptions contain many details concerning information, equipment, and working processes — details which may be irrelevant in relation to, for instance, having to decide for or against a suggested innovation.

The above can be summarized by saying that several types of descriptions are necessary. It is important to be able to vary perspective and working process in order to meet different objectives, needs, and interests.

Figure 9.5 The main direction of movement in systems development.

9.2 Top-down — an illusion?

Many different description techniques and tools have been advertised with slogans containing the term 'top-down'. But what does it mean to employ a top-down approach in descriptions? Top-down is a confusing concept — the word covers a number of different meanings. The techniques advertised with this slogan sum up relevant experience as well as poor ideas, but as a means to characterize the description process the concept is meaningless. This section will present some examples of what are usually called top-down techniques. Afterwards it will look at what actually happens when we make descriptions. Top-down apparently indicates a movement, but what are the different directions one can move in during the description work?

Top-down covers many different meanings

Sometimes top-down denotes a way to work out descriptions. Different methods require that the descriptions are worked out top-down. This may mean that you must start by making an overall description, and then work down into the details. At other times top-down means that you start with concepts from the users' world, and then work towards more technical concepts. There have, however, been many objections to the notion that it should be possible to work out a description by starting from totality and then moving towards detail. To get an overall picture you must know the details and concrete situations. This means that the description process will shift focus from totality to detail and back again. It may also be problematic to work one-sidedly from the users' world towards more technical issues. How would it be possible to delimit the relevant aspects in the users' world? And how can you evaluate the various technical proposals?

At other times top-down denotes a specific way of programming. The programmer starts with an overall description of the algorithm and the associated data structures, and from here he proceeds by stepwise refinements. However, it is impossible to work in this way. The original algorithm will change as you work down into the details. The programmer will, in other words, get new ideas for an overall design of the program while he works with the details.

Top-down also denotes an overall way of realizing the computer system. You start by programming a skeleton system connecting all the modules. Then you program the individual modules. This makes it possible to test the modules' interaction with the totality as you go along. This way of using the concept top-down is not as problematic as the ones described above.

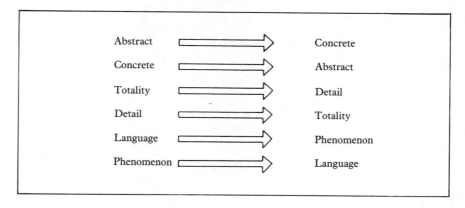

Figure 9.6   Possible directions of movement in the description process.

Top-down is usually nonsense
But the question still remains: what is actually up, and what is down when the term top-down is used? The examples listed above illustrate that the words are given quite different and very problematic meanings in different contexts. The problem is that the various directions of the description work cannot be summed up in a simple distinction between up and down. The following text will look at a describer who looks at a phenomenon — and it will take a closer look at some of the different choices the describer may take in the description process. Figure 9.6 sums up the different directions of movement discussed below.

The abstract and the concrete

Design and realization is a question of connecting two worlds
During design and realization one necessarily and always works both from the concrete towards the abstract and from the abstract towards the concrete, because the descriptions aim at bringing together two different concrete worlds (see Figure 9.7). On one hand there is the users' situation and a vision formulated on the basis of problems in the user organization. On the other hand there is the applied computer equipment which is understood with the aid of concepts from programming languages, database systems, and operating systems. The vision of the new system is an abstraction of the problems in the user organization, and the resulting computer-based system is a concretization of this vision. If top-down means working from the abstract towards the concrete, this working practice is a practical impossibility during the design and realization activities.

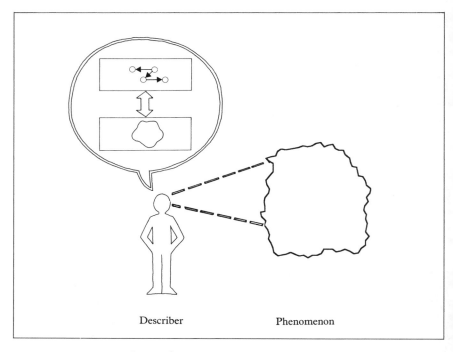

Figure 9.7   Abstract ⇐ ⇒ concrete.

A distinction between whether the describer moves from the abstract towards the concrete, or from the concrete towards the abstract, is a distinction between what level the describer sees the phenomenon on. The describer looks at the phenomenon as a whole, or at a specific limited part of the phenomenon, hence achieving a more or less abstract understanding.

In the beginning of his or her investigations the describer will receive an immense amount of impressions which will result in a very concrete, but perhaps confusing understanding of the phenomenon. By selecting, organizing, and simplifying, the describer can obtain a more systematic but abstract understanding. If the describer's task is to work out a report on the various applications of computer technology in a company, he or she may start by being shown around the company and talking to the various employees. In this way the describer will get a number of different, but not necessarily coherent, impressions. On this background the describer will process his or her understanding, return to the employees with new questions, employ new concepts and ways of looking at things — and after a while the describer will understand selected patterns and correlations. In this way the describer moves from a spontaneous, concrete understanding towards a simpler and more abstract one. If the describer has the opportunity to work for a longer period with the problem, the different abstract understandings may become a part of a comprehensive, concrete understanding of the totality. People with long experience within an area obviously have both a concrete and coherent understanding of the area in question. In brief, a concrete understanding is rich and manifold, while an abstract understanding is simplified and detached from totality.

Totality and detail

An overall picture requires understanding of detail and vice versa

Knowledge of details is a prerequisite of obtaining an overall picture. And an overall picture is a prerequisite of selecting the relevant details. It is a principle that neither analysis nor design activities can move unidirectionally from totality towards detail (principle P8, Chapter 3). If top-down means to work from totality towards detail, this working practice cannot be recommended during analysis and design work.

The choice between moving from totality towards detail, or from detail towards totality is a question of how the describer shifts focus during the description work. Whereas the movement between the abstract and the concrete is a question of the level at which the describer understands a given, limited reality, the former is a question of how the describer's attention shifts between different parts of the phenomenon.

If, for instance, during the analysis of an office you start by getting an overview by talking with the office manager, and then go on to talk with individual employees on lower levels, we would say that you move from totality towards detail. If, on the other hand, you start by analysing the working processes of individual people, and then try to get an overall picture of how all the tasks in the office are solved, you move from detail towards totality. (See Figure 9.8.)

Language and phenomenon

An analysis may be planned with the objective that the participants together should build up words and concepts increasing their

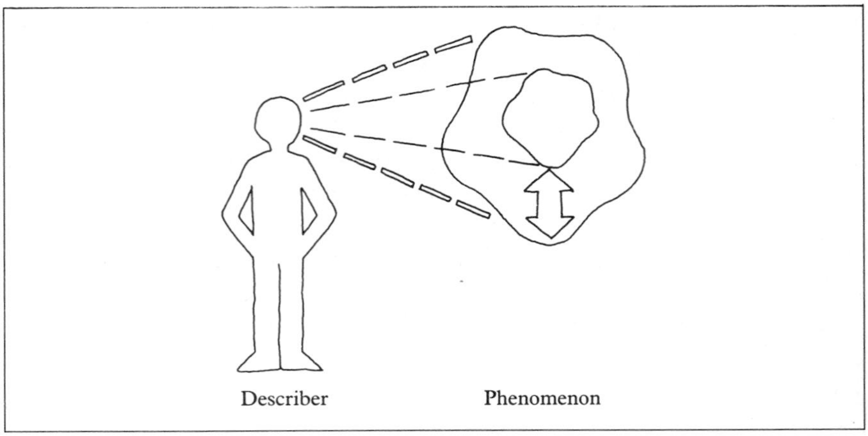

Figure 9.8 Totality ⇦ ⇨ detail.

understanding of similar phenomena. The objective may be that this understanding should be a shared platform improving the quality of the design process. The system developers can improve their ability to understand and disseminate visions by participating in an analysis process like that, and the users will find it easier to understand the system developers' suggestions, and they will find it easier to formulate their requirements.

The describer moves from language towards phenomenon when the objective of the description is to understand the phenomenon he or she is facing. The describer employs well-known words and concepts to understand the phenomenon. Movement from the phenomenon towards language, on the other hand, means that the describer creates new words and concepts on the basis of his or her understanding of the phenomenon. In this way the describer is able to understand similar phenomena in a new way later on. (See Figure 9.9.)

In education situations one typically works with movements from phenomenon towards language. If students are given the assignment to analyse the working processes in an office, this is not because it is important that they understand this particular office. They are asked to do so because they must accumulate words and concepts which will enable them to understand other offices and other analysis processes later on. The program library is an expression of the same movement. Procedures which have been developed in one application situation are saved as extensions of the applied programming languages to make the programming work easier in other situations.

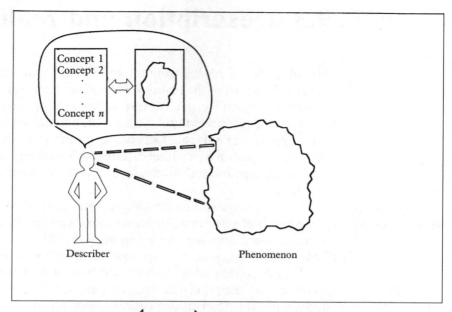

Figure 9.9 Language ⟸ ⟹ phenomenon.

Exercise 9.2

Discuss directions of movement in practice

Discuss the analysis and design activities in your last project and characterize the directions of movement in the project. When did you work in the following directions?

- From the abstract towards the concrete.
- From the concrete towards the abstract.
- From totality towards detail.
- From detail towards totality.
- From language towards the phenomenon.
- From the phenomenon towards language.

Would it have been an advantage to organize the work differently? What were the important arguments?

9.3 Description and reality

The objective of most computer systems is — in some way or other — to model a part of the reality surrounding them. An inventory system models a physical storehouse and movements of goods to or from this storehouse. A process control system must contain a model of the process it is supposed to control. Depending on the objective of the system, emphasis is put on describing different selected aspects of reality. The applied description techniques and tools have a decisive effect on this selection.

Descriptions are interpretations of reality

Computer systems contain a description of reality. This description is the result of selections, interpretations and simplifications. Various forms of abstractions have been employed during the description process. This section will take a closer look at these forms of abstraction.

People participating in the description process understand reality according to their perspective. Others, who are going to read and understand the descriptions later on, will interpret them according to their own perspectives. And the interpretation of a description will change as the conceptual world and perspectives of those who are interpreting the descriptions change.

Description and reality. Any description expresses an interpretation of reality.

An example is a system to support the administration of a company's car park. The cost of operation and maintenance of each car is registered on the basis of invoices from the garages. The invoices are described in the system by a number of records. The original description of the record concept was based on an economy perspective. A record contains information about the cost of a repair job. However, the system is used both by the mechanics, who must know the maintenance history of the car, and by the staff in the administration, who must negotiate with insurance companies, and who must make sure that the cars are called in for service checks. In practice this means that the price of a repair job is made subordinate to information about the type of repair in question. Important types of repair jobs like service checks, damages, and undercarriage treatments are given special treatment when registering records. The record concept slowly changes meaning. Gradually there is less and less sense in comparing the actual registration of invoices with the original objective. The economist and the mechanic have widely differing conceptions of what information is important.

This was an example of how the interpretation of concepts changes over time. The following will look at how the descriptions are made. It will look at how concepts are created through different forms of abstractions. By evaluating a concrete description tool it can be seen what form of abstraction the tool supports. This may reveal how applicable the tool is, and may also give an idea of how the description should be kept up to date as the concepts change.

Classification and exemplification

The type concept supports classification

Classification results in a concept denoting a number of phenomena. The concept 'purchase order' may, for instance, denote that an organization has ordered goods from a supplier. Exemplification, on the other hand, selects a specific phenomenon denoted by a concept. An example of a purchase order would be Order No. 851154, ordering 5,000 screws from a specific supplier. In programming languages and data-base languages classification is supported by the type concept. Figure 9.10 illustrates that fundamental concepts about phenomena are created through classification. These concepts form the basis of creating different hierarchies of concepts through generalization and aggregation as described below.

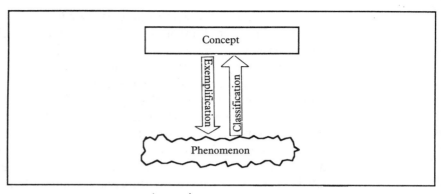

Figure 9.10   Classification ⟺ exemplification.

Generalization and specialization

Generalization is rarely supported

Generalization results in a concept covering a number of different concepts. One may, for instance, create the concept 'order' to cover both 'purchase order' and 'repair order'. Or the concept 'vehicle' to cover 'car', 'bicycle', and 'motor bike'. Specialization, on the other hand, means that one or more specific concepts are formed on the basis of a given concept. One may, for instance, have the concept 'internal repair order' covering repair orders in one's own garage. Or the concept 'passenger car' covering a special type of car. The properties linked to a concept created through generalization of other concepts are shared by these other concepts. The properties linked to the concept 'order' are thus linked to both 'purchase order' and 'repair order'. Generalization is not normally supported in programming languages and data-base languages. However, there are several languages which support specialization. (See Figure 9.11.)

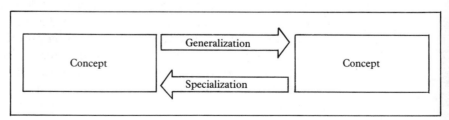

Figure 9.11   Generalization ⟺ specialization.

Aggregation and decomposition

*Records and
hierarchical
databases
support
aggregation*

Aggregation results in a concept describing compound phenomena. The phenomena are built up of parts corresponding to other concepts. The concept 'car', for instance, describes a compound phenomenon consisting of parts corresponding to the concepts 'wheel', 'steering wheel', 'engine', and 'body'. Decomposition, on the other hand, divides a concept into subconcepts corresponding to a splitting up of the corresponding phenomenon. 'Purchase order' may be split up into 'delivery date', 'supplier', 'quantity', and 'type of goods'. Aggregation and decomposition express something about the correlation between different concepts (see Figure 9.12). The same concept may enter into different aggregates. Aggregation is supported by record structures and hierarchies in data bases.

Concepts are fuzzy

With respect to programming languages and data bases, concepts are expected to be precisely defined. It is necessary to be able to determine whether a given phenomenon is covered by the concept. It is found annoying that the users are unable to give a precise definition of their concepts. Exceptions and borderline cases have a tendency to pop up after the system has been taken into use. This is not because the users lack understanding of their own work. It is because reality has been given more structure than it can take. Only very few concepts have sharp and well-defined borders. The users do not have a precise definition of a purchase order, and it will often be difficult to come up with a definition covering the use of the term in practice. Instead the users typically use a number of examples as a basis for their understanding of a given concept.

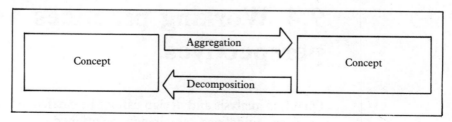

Figure 9.12   Aggregation ⟺ decomposition.

It is necessary to create concepts and try to delimit them when describing a computer system. But it is important to remember that the computer system reflects an interpretation of reality. The interpretation will change, even if the programs and data structures remain the same. The interpretation will change in an interaction between application of the system and development of concepts in the user environment. It is also important to remember that concepts which are difficult to define are handled more efficiently by people than by machines.

Figure 9.13 summarizes the correlation between the various ways in which concepts may be created through abstractions and concretizations. Aggregation, generalization, and classification are all forms of abstraction. Decomposition and specialization are the corresponding forms of concretization.

Exercise 9.3

Analyse the formation of concepts in practice

Analyse some of the programming or system description languages applied in your company. Which of the various forms of abstraction and concretization do the languages support?

Do you still apply some of the forms of abstraction and concretization which the languages fail to support? Would it be advantageous to have several ways of expressing these?

9.4 Working practices and perspectives

Qualified analysis and design cannot be carried out directly according to given guidelines, as already mentioned several times. Qualified

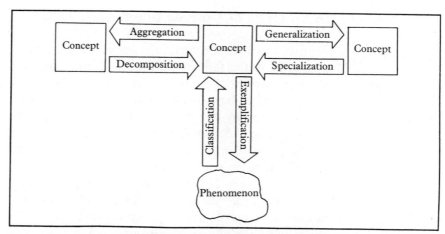

Figure 9.13   Forms of abstraction and corresponding forms of concretization.

analysis and design first and foremost requires experience, intuition, imagination, and common sense. It is consequently recommended that you vary your working practice as well as your perspective in your description work. It would have been helpful to present a suitable selection of existing description methods. But there are many methods and it is difficult to give a satisfactory presentation within the limits of this book. Instead some main types of working practices and perspectives will be looked at more generally, and you can base your description work on these.

Working practices and perspectives are closely connected

Perspectives and working practices are closely connected. A working practice denotes the procedure applied in the description work. The working practice may be consciously organized, or it may be an expression of tradition and experience. In any case, any working practice implies a specific perspective in the description work. A perspective may be characterized by the choice of standpoint, by the selection of properties of the phenomenon in question, and by the way the observed properties are interpreted. A specific perspective invites a specific working practice, and the perspective is typically realized with specific description techniques and tools. When in the following some of the main types of working practices and perspectives are looked at, therefore, two views of the same thing are obtained. The aim is to point out some of the many different possibilities for varying your descriptions.

Main types of working practices

Figure 9.14 lists the various types of working practices which will be discussed in the following. The list is not exhaustive, but it indicates some important alternatives. In other words, the figure gives some of the options to be considered when organizing the description work.

Actor or observer?

The primary distinction is between the describer observing a given phenomenon — and the describer being personally engaged and involved in the phenomenon he or she is describing and changing.

Working practices inviting the describer to play the role of an actor are illustrated in Chapter 6. When a project group maps the situation in a project, they do this in order to understand and change their own situation. Even though mapping is presented as something directed at the situation of the project group, this working practice can easily be applied in cooperation with users in relation to their situation, and thus become part of the project's analysis and design activities. It is also possible to look upon systems description with the users as a working practice where the users participate actively in the description work

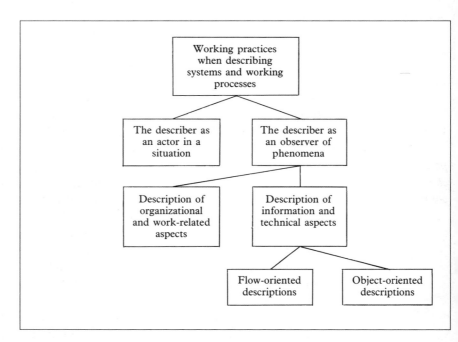

Figure 9.14   Some of the main types of working practices.

— not only by contributing to a better understanding, but also by influencing and changing their own situation. This technique was described in more detail in Chapter 8.

The normal case is, however, that those who make the descriptions are not personally involved in the situation they are describing and changing. The describer acts as an observer of the working situation of other people. Organizational, financial, and political aspects often set limits which render this type of working practice the only possible one to follow.

Focus on technical or organizational aspects?

When limiting the discussion to the describer as an observer of a phenomenon, there are two main types of working practices: those where focus is put on organizational and work-related aspects, and those where focus is put on information and technical issues. Obviously there are always both organizational and technical issues. The crucial question is where emphasis is put.

If emphasis is on the technical aspects of the system, the problem to be solved by the project is normally seen as given. The system is not so much looked on as forming part of an organization, but emphasis is laid rather on the technical complexity of the task. This is the natural way to work in developing systems software and technically oriented application software. But it is a principle that technically oriented analysis and design entails the risk of overlooking important aspects of the problem and easily leads to a perfect solution to the wrong problem (principle P6, Chapter 3).

If emphasis is on the organizational changes, the technical aspects are pushed into the background. The typical assumption is that the problem is technically relatively simple. Organizationally oriented practices are based on the assumption that the technical issues that arise can be handled, or that the assignment is to adapt an existing technical solution to the current organization. There are relatively few actual methods for describing organizational and work-oriented aspects. There is, however, a lot of literature on organizations, and on work and work organization. As a first step away from focusing on the technical aspects, it may be a good idea to draw on some of this knowledge in the analysis and design work.

Flow-oriented or object-oriented descriptions?

The majority of literature on analysis and design concentrates on information and technical aspects. Here we may distinguish between flow-oriented and object-oriented descriptions. The flow-oriented descriptions focus on the information or data flows, and you typically work from totality towards detail. You start by delimiting the system in a first, overall diagram — and from there you work towards the detail. An example is Yourdon and DeMarco's method for structured analysis and design. The opposite of this is the object-oriented form of description. Here a number of concepts are first created, linked to the phenomena that are about to be described and changed, then the totality in question is delimited and described. The object-oriented working practice thus includes both movement from totality towards detail and the other way around. An example is Jackson's design method.

Main types of perspectives

Table 9.1 lists a number of different perspectives to be applied in the description work. The list will be discussed in the following. As was the case concerning working practices, these types can be viewed as options to be considered when organizing the description work. You will find a more detailed presentation of the perspective concept in Chapter 8.

	Focus on the individual	Focus on the collective
Focus on the computer system	Computer-based man–machine interaction	Computer-based information systems
Focus on the application situation	Work processes supported by computer-based tools	Communication and interaction through computer-based media

Table 9.1   List of some main types of perspectives on the application of computer technology.

The individual and the machine

The first type of perspective focuses on computer-based man–machine interaction. The important thing is the individual's work with the computer system. What data are fed into the machine, and which are taken out? How are these data structured and formatted? What equipment and techniques are applied in the interaction between the individual and the machine? The main interest of the designer is to create a smooth and well-functioning user interface. The perspective centres on the individual, and it is of no importance what the various data express or represent.

The tool   The other type of perspective focuses on work processes supported by computer-based tools. The individual still plays a central role, but the important thing now is the work-related aspects into which the computer system enters. The computer system is seen as a tool to support the individual's performance of the actual task. Qualifications, traditions, and quality of work are put in the foreground — and the computer application is consequently seen in relation to this. The designer's main interest is to create a working situation where the user of the computer system can concentrate on the actual task. To obtain this the designer must, among other things, create a smooth and well-functioning user interface, but on an overall level the designer must ensure interaction between the task, the user's abilities and knowledge, and the computer system.

The information system   The third type of perspective focuses on computer-based information systems. The important thing here is the collected system of hardware, software, and users — with emphasis on the computer system. Interest centres on the production, processing and storing of information, and the way this is practised in cooperation between the users and the computer system. The designer's main interest is to create a smooth and well-functioning totality of users and computer systems, which together have the required information-processing capacity. The perspective is collective, but it is unimportant what the various informations express and represent.

The medium   The fourth and last type of perspective focuses on communication and interaction through computer-based media. This perspective also looks at the collective of users, but with main emphasis on objectives, actions, and interests expressed through the computer-based media. The fundamental interest is linked to the communication and interaction between people, and the computer system is merely seen as one of many ways to communicate. The designer's main interest is to create an organizationally well-functioning totality into which the computer system can enter as a medium for communication and interaction between its users.

The working practices and the perspectives have been described in a rough and simplified manner. In practice no one would use only one of these specific working practices or perspectives. On the other hand, it may be turned up-side-down and the question asked: who, in practice, makes use of the scope for variation described above? The idea of this chapter has been to contribute to a better understanding of the fundamental elements of design and analysis work — and to encourage people to use their imagination to ensure more variation in the practical work.

Exercise 9.4

Discuss analysis and design in practice

Discuss a number of projects and characterize the applied working practices and perspectives on the basis of Figures 9.14 and 9.15. Evaluate whether the projects were successful, or whether more variation in the description work would have been desirable. If the latter is the case, then clarify the alternatives.

Further reading

This chapter is partly based on Mathiassen (1981). Naur (1985) argues convincingly for the importance of intuition in practical systems development. The concepts in Section 9.3 are from Knudsen and Thomsen (1985). The different types of perspectives are described in more detail by Kammersgaard (1985), Ehn and Kyng (1984), and Andersen (1985). For further study there is a rich literature on description of systems and working processes. Here you will find many suggestions for using the various working practices and perspectives. From the literature list in the back of this book we can mention the following: Blegen and Nylehn (1974), Checkland (1981), Ciborra (1981), Davis and Olson (1984), DeMarco (1979), Galbraith (1973), Gustavsen (1977), Holbæk-Hanssen *et al.* (1975), Jackson (1983), Lucas (1985), Martin and McClure (1985), Mumford (1985) and Yourdon (1982).

10 Avoid permanent firefighting

Permanent firefighting impedes new development

The moments of truth will come during test, conversion, and operation

Things rarely come to a head during analysis and design. The project is either well organized enough to regulate events if problems should arise, or the problems are put off to be solved later. However, in connection with test, conversion, and production you will be confronted with the results of all the analysis and design activities. The objective of a system development project is to create and to change. Therefore you will not get a correct picture of the quality of the analysis and design work until the changes are put into effect in realization activities. Realization includes activities such as the following:

- Coding programs.
- Debugging and testing programs.
- Taking new or changed computer systems into use.
- Introducing changes in the user organization.
- Training in the operation of new computer systems and the performance of new work functions.
- Training that aims at developing the qualifications in the user organization.
- Conversion.

It is a principle that product-oriented reflection (analysis and design) and realization affect each other and should be performed concurrently (principle P2, Chapter 3). During the realization activities mistakes made during analysis and design come to light, and the realization activities may result in constructive ideas for new designs. However, project plans rarely allow for the necessary time to make use of experiences resulting from renewed reflection and realization.

In many projects developing new systems some of the participants are still responsible for maintaining old systems. They may be the only ones who can actually do this because of insufficient documentation and incomprehensible programs. Plans often fail to set aside time for firefighting situations which arise when new systems are put in production. These fires are caused by program errors and demands for adaptation. When the fires start burning, there is a tendency to rush into fighting them, i.e. realization without reflection. In cases like this, new problems will easily show up. The projects developing new systems are neglected and may develop into new seats of fire. Many system developers feel that they are on safe and well-known territory in firefighting situations. Thus firefighting is — more or less consciously — given higher priority than the uncertain work of developing a new system.

This chapter will discuss the problems arising in connection with realization activities — especially as a consequence of inadequate interaction between realization and reflection. Sections 10.1 and 10.2 discuss how the problems may give rise to crises in a project which may be hard to solve. Sections 10.3—5 look at three activities: test, conversion, and maintenance. These are the situations where the system developers experience the moments of truth, and where a lot of firefighting is done.

10.1 Save your reserves for a crisis

Any project has reserves, the most important ones being human resources. These reserves come from the following:

* Working over-time.
* Postponing long-term work, for instance management activities, design, and training.
* Getting more people into the project, either from other projects in the development organization, or external consultants.
* Cutting down on the quality of the products and services.
* Postponing deliveries.

Through using reserves you may solve an acute crisis. Acute crises may be caused by the following:

* Resource failures, for instance machine stops, illness, resignations, the development organization 'stealing' people to do other activities.
* Acute increase in the amount of work.
* Delayed deliveries of products developed in parallel.
* Revealed errors and defects in a product or a service which was supposed to be all right.
* A serious underestimation of the extent of an activity, or a faulty evaluation of the conditions for performing the activity.

Acute crises may arise in any project, and it is good to have reserves. However, reserves should be used for only a short period of time, as the use of reserves has two disadvantages. Firstly, there are no longer

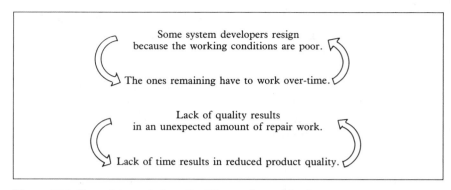

Figure 10.1 Two vicious circles of self-increasing crisis phenomena.

reserves available if another crisis should occur on top of the first one. Secondly, the use of reserves increases the probability of new crises. This may result in a vicious circle of self-increasing crisis phenomena. Figure 10.1 illustrates two simple examples of vicious circles. In practice there will often be a number of crisis phenomena in a vicious circle.

Some organizations find themselves in a permanent crisis. They are caught by a vicious circle where there are never any surplus resources to even consider how to get out of the crisis. Some system developers work in a permanent state of crisis as well. They run around fighting fires. They correct errors and defects in running programs, give advice and guidance about systems that are not documented, etc. This may give them a certain amount of respect. They are praised because they are such good problem solvers. And they often deserve the praise — these system developers are trained firefighters. However, people seem to forget that many of the problems are a direct result of the firefighters' own working practices.

10.2 How do you get out of a permanent crisis?

Prevention does not solve present problems

What can you do when you are in the middle of a permanent crisis? The easiest answer would be to prevent future crises. However, this is a poor answer when you are stuck in the situation.

The general answer is that you should identify the central problems,

Firefighting. You must identify the central problems and solve them — otherwise the firefighting will continue.

disengage resources, and use them to solve these problems. It is of no avail to cheat where any of these elements are concerned — this would only result in more firefighting.

To identify the central problems, you must map the situation. For this you may employ diagnostic and ecological maps (see Chapter 6). But how can you be sure that you are in a permanent crisis, and not just busy? The general symptoms are that you use your reserves permanently. You will typically not have time for the long-term activities you would have liked to carry out. There might, for instance, not be time for training, planning, design, analysis, and quality assurance.

The diagnostic and ecological maps will reveal a number of phenomena which mutually enhance each other. There are different circular dependencies between phenomena. However, be careful in your interpretations of these circles. Not all circles are vicious. In most organizations there is a balance between the qualifications of the system developers, the degree of complexity in the activities, the quality of the products, etc. These phenomena also manifest themselves as a circle on a map. This does not, however, mean that the organization is in a permanent crisis. The decisive criterion is that the reserves are permanently in use. If you can find time to read this book, you are not in serious trouble.

Disengage resources. Let it burn.

The easiest solution to a permanent crisis is to call in help from outside. But usually you must make do with the resources inside the project. Then you must disengage resources. This can be done in only one way. You must let some of the problems lie. You must let some of the fires burn down. This can be a very hard thing to do. But here, as in any investment, you must decide to make do with a little less now, so that you can have a lot more in the future. It may, for instance, become necessary to give the users a poorer service for a while. You might decide only to correct disastrous errors, and to ignore minor errors and inexpediencies.

The disengaged resources made available should be spent on solving central problems, i.e. problems whose solutions have a beneficial effect on other parts of the situation, especially in the form of disengaging other resources.

Exercise 10.1

Work out a crisis-solving plan

What do you do when you are in the middle of a permanent crisis?

- Have you ever been in a permanent crisis?

- How did you get out of it?

- Evaluate the general answer:
  (a) Identify the central problems.
  (b) Make resources available.
  (c) Solve central problems.

- Why are all three elements necessary when you wish to get out of a permanent crisis?

Try to apply the mapping technique described in Chapter 6 to a crisis you have experienced. Identify the central problems, draw up the possibilities for action and work out a crisis-solving plan.

10.3 Tests do not solve any problems

Plan repairs   A system does not get any better from being tested, nor does a service improve by being tested. The only thing that will improve the quality of the products and services is the correction of the errors and defects revealed by the test. Everyone remembers to set aside time for tests in the plans, but many people forget to set aside time to repair the errors and defects revealed by the tests. If you plan to test, this must be because you expect to find errors and defects. But in that case you ought also to have time to correct them.

How many resources should be set aside for repairs? This is inherently a difficult question to answer. You do not know the extent and nature of the errors and defects beforehand. The whole project is planned with the intention that there are no errors and defects when the system is tested.

The best you can do is to employ the extrapolation technique (see estimation, Chapter 5), so that you set aside a certain proportion of the resources that are used for developing a product or planning a service. The size of the proportion depends on a number of factors. Literature of systems development mentions figures up to 20 per cent of the total development time. The wisest thing to do is to accumulate your own experience based on organization-specific conditions.

Once you are in a situation where the test reveals more errors than expected, you must try to fight your way out of the problem. This situation requires a lot of the management function. The situation requires thorough evaluation and regulation. If you choose to put an error-ridden system into operation rather than postponing delivery, you risk ending up in a worse situation than the one you started out with. It might be necessary to do this anyway, but the consequences should be considered carefully. Resources should be set aside to support the system.

It is a principle that tests do not solve any problems. Therefore you should plan with time for repairs, and thus prevent permanent firefighting situations (principle P9, Chapter 3).

10.4 Conversion should be planned carefully

Conversion is the actual innovative activity in systems development. The activity includes technical and functional conversion. The technical conversion consists of changing the computer system and the user organization, as follows:

- Train the operating staff.
- Put new software and hardware into operation.
- Move data from the old to the new system.
- Establish provisional interfaces between the old and the new system.

The functional conversion consists of changing the user organization as follows:

- Train the users.
- Change the manual working processes.
- Register existing manual files.
- Establish provisional interfaces to the computer system currently being changed.

In many projects the user organization is responsible for the functional conversion. The system developers should, however, check the users' conversion plans and follow the functional conversion. Two reasons for this are that the development organization is more experienced where conversion is concerned, and that the coordination between the technical and the functional conversion is important.

Conversion is a once-only service which usually cannot be tested in its totality. Many parts cannot be realistically tested individually. Planning should therefore be done with plenty in reserve, both in the development organization and in the user organization. It is possible to push the problems back and forth between the system developers and the users. This should preferably result in solutions, not conflicts. It is a principle that qualified realization requires careful planning of the conversion. The overall design should include the overall conversion plan (principle P10, Chapter 3). When designing new systems, you should consider how you would like the conversion to take place.

Do not convert
at new year

Conversion often includes a lot of parallel activities that are difficult to control. Many people choose to make the conversion simpler by taking their starting point in, for instance, a well-defined system state. A state like that typically occurs with the commencement of a new year. This is very inadvisable. Firstly, delivery cannot be postponed for less than one whole year, which is often unacceptable to the users. Secondly, other activities at this time of year take away a lot of resources. It is much easier to regulate the project if conversion does not need to take place at this time. It should be possible to postpone the conversion. The activities that are to take place just before the conversion are difficult to plan. The test may reveal surprises. The conversion may also reveal errors, making it necessary to return to the old system while the repairs are made.

Unprofessional conversion may result in a permanent crisis. The system developers risk getting stuck in production because no one else can understand the system, and in maintenance, because the users sneak in requirements for changes among the errors to be corrected. Test and conversion will give the users ideas for changes. But it is important to stick to the original design while test and conversion is taking place. It is far better to plan with a follow-up project than to make hasty changes during test and conversion.

10.5 Maintenance made interesting

Maintenance denotes various things. The kind of work depends on the type of system and on the development organization's relations to the user organization. If there are close relations between the user organization and the development organization, there will typically be permanent maintenance. The users' requirements for new reports and smaller changes will be met as they arise. Another kind of maintenance is the correction of errors that are decisive for the operation of the system. This is typically performed under heavy pressure and in an atmosphere of impending catastrophe. It is usually the system developers who developed the system who are assigned to correct this sort of error.

Identifying errors often gives the finder a lot of prestige — especially if the error is found in other people's products.

The former kind of maintenance will now be considered. This is the kind that is often perceived as boring by most system developers, and as something that should be avoided. Many organizations therefore asign this task to system developers with a low status. One has a low status if one is new in the organization, or if one is considered a poor system developer. This obviously affects the motivation of the person who is given the job.

Why does maintenance have a low status?

Why is maintenance such a bore? Well, firstly there are the following points concerning the working conditions:

- You are expected to work with people who have a low status in the organization.

- The maintenance might be allocated to several of the original developers, who maintain their individual parts of the system while doing their actual work, which is to develop a new system. This results in poor communication in the maintenance group.

- Maintenance is often not organized in projects, but rather as current routine work which gets the attention of management only when something goes wrong.

- Maintenance is given low priority where resources are concerned, because only new development projects result in new income.

- There may be a backlog of change requests.

- The users may be used to unprofessional maintenance.

Secondly, there are factors such as the following, concerning the quality of the products you are working with:

- There may be no documentation, or there may be lots of incoherent, out-of-date development documentation.

- The programs may be mutilated across their original structure because the programmers who changed them did not understand them.

- Out-dated programming style may render the programs hard to understand.

- The programs may have been moved from one computer to another, so that input and output is performed in obscure ways.

- There may be many errors in the programs which are avoided during careful production, but which appear if changes are made elsewhere.

- Unreachable code and obsolete data items may be preserved because no programmer dared to delete them, and did not bother to document that this was what happened.

- Programs may not have been converted to normal production; they may require the programmer's presence when run.

The maintenance programmer is asking for trouble

Apparently there are many reasons for looking down your nose at maintenance work — you cannot learn from it. However, this is quite wrong. It is a very instructive task to change the conditions described above. Maintenance programmers complaining about not being able to get started on challenging assignments because all their time is taken up by maintenance, are asking for trouble. They are in the middle of all the challenges, but fail to take them up.

- Work out a standard for documentation. Take your starting point in the minimum standard in Chapter 7.

- Build up the renovated documentation independent of the old, unreliable documentation.

- Reduce the list of change requests to a realistic size.

- Allocate routine work to the production department or to the users.

Figure 10.2 Advice concerning system renovation.

What can be done then? The solution is to gradually renovate the programs and the documentation. Figure 10.2 gives some advice for how to do this. Chapter 12 will describe an example of how a maintenance group started to solve their problems.

Exercise 10.2

How can the maintenance work be improved?

- How is the maintenance work carried out in your organization? What is the status of this kind of work? Why?

- How can the conditions for the maintenance work be improved?
  (a) By improved product quality.
  (b) By improved organization of the maintenance work.
  (c) By improved working practices in maintenance.

  Evaluate the advice in Figure 10.2.

- Is maintenance suitable work for new employees in the organization?

Further reading

You will not find much literature on maintenance, but you might find Parnas and Clements (1985) and Naur (1984) inspiring and provoking.

Part III

Changing Working Practices in Systems Development

11 Strategies for changing working practices

The results should show up in the projects

Professional systems development has two important characteristics. Firstly, active and competent project management. A project should be established systematically, successive versions of the plan should currently be worked out in the course of the project, status should be evaluated, working practices should — if necessary — be changed. Secondly, the system developers should have the opportunity and the willingness to increase their own repertoire of working practices.

Building up a repertoire of working practices

So far this book has discussed what systems development is, and how systems development should be performed. This last part of the book deals with how the individual system developer, project group, and development organization can create and change working practices in systems development.

When changing working practices, it is necessary to be aware of the interaction between the condition and the strategic options (see Figure 11.1). The conditions delimit the possible strategy. The strategy will also — when applied — affect the conditions. This chapter discusses the individual elements in this interaction. Sections 11.1−3 look at the conditions. Section 11.4 discusses some traditional strategies, and Section 11.5 contains our suggestion for how changing working practices should be tackled.

Exercise 11.1

Analyse how changing working practices are tackled today

Consider the following questions about your development organization:

- Who are the change agents?
- How is the change work organized?
- How many resources are spent on change work?
- What objectives are formulated?
- What activities are being performed?
- Are the objectives met?
- If not, what are the reasons?

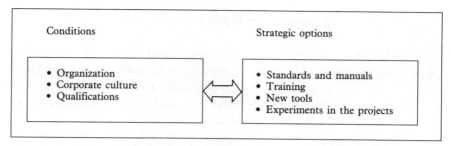

Figure 11.1   Conditions and strategic options for changing working practices.

11.1 Who are the change agents?

Things only happen if somebody feels responsible for making them happen. The five different groups in a development organization who might feel responsible for changing working practices, are as follows:

- The development management.
- The project leaders.
- A staff function.
- External consultants.
- The system developers themselves.

Development management

The development manager is formally responsible for what happens in the organization, including the change of working practices. However, the manager will typically not have the time and the opportunity to ensure that working practices are changed. The manager still plays a very important role, however, because he or she is responsible for giving priority to activities and for allocating resources, and his or her actions affect the attitudes in the organization.

The project leader

Who pushes the
project leader?
The project leader is responsible for what happens in the project. The project leader is responsible for making sure that the project is a learning process for its participants, that the employed working practices are expedient, and that the necessary qualifications are available. If the project leader is interested in changing working practices, he or she may succeed and come up with good results in the project. However, there are limits to how far one can go along this route. Firstly, there will only be a limited degree of continuity in the change activities. The dynamics will disappear every time a project is terminated. Secondly, an important part of professional working practices is project management. If the individual project leader is responsible for changing working practices, who will then push the project leader?

A staff function

Many development organizations have a staff function that is responsible for organizational changes. The function may be called the methods department, the training department, or the quality assurance department. On the face of it this function seems a reasonable way of organizing things, but in practice there are a number of problems. Firstly, there is the staff. Methods specialists should be competent and experienced practitioners — if they are not, no one will listen to them. However, management might be reluctant to remove the required number of productive people from their daily work. Secondly, there is the question of effective means. How does the methods department get its ideas across? The methods department's own efforts are given low priority on a day-to-day basis compared to the work in the projects. In an attempt at getting its ideas across, the methods department may issue directives, or write extensive manuals. However, one cannot promote a professional working practice by merely telling the system developers how they should do their work. Systems development is more than just routine work. Systems development requires the ability to choose and act on the basis of the situation in the individual projects. Here directives have little, or even negative, effect.

A methods department must take as its starting point the needs of the projects. If the methods department is staffed with competent people, and if these people succeed in integrating the methods work in the projects, good results can be obtained. It is not enough just to establish a methods department.

Consultants

External consultants have the advantage that all their efforts can be directed at improving working practices. The reason for this is that they cannot be drawn into the daily work. Furthermore, a consultant is a more mobile resource. However, this is also the reason why you cannot make the consultant responsible for changing working practices. You can, however, hire consultants who can contribute with new ideas to the organization. External people are a source of inspiration and provocation.

The system developers

The system developers know what goes on

The most radical solution would be to place the responsibility for changing working practices with the system developers themselves. This would mean that it would be the working practices and traditions relevant in the opinion of the system developers that are put up for revision. This will increase the motivation and the resulting effects. Another argument in favour of this approach is that it is the system developers themselves who have the best opportunity to integrate the changes in the projects. If responsibility is placed with the system developers alone, however, the conditions for changing working practices will be poor. There will be no protection against the daily pressure from the actual project work. The changes will thus all too easily be set aside. Section 11.5 contains a suggestion for how the changes could be organized. In this approach the efforts of the five groups mentioned above are combined into an effective strategy.

11.2 The corporate culture: incentive or impediment?

The corporate culture consists of norms, values, attitudes, formal and informal rules, traditions, rituals, and myths that characterize the company and give it its identity, and that makes the company different from other companies. The corporate culture is a decisive factor in the efforts to change working practices. It may act either as an incentive or as an impediment.

Figure 11.2 lists a number of important questions that should be asked when the changes are planned. The figure also contains a number of possible answers. The questions may be a help when studying the culture in a company.

Come up with quick results, and encourage professional discussions

The change work must be adapted to the corporate culture. However, it will often prove necessary to influence and change the corporate culture to facilitate the change work. But how can you influence something as intangible as a culture? Actions have a greater effect than words. Hence it is better to be able to refer to successful examples of changed working practices, or to concrete experience, than it is to postulate a number of advantages. That is why it is important to ensure quick results.

Professional discussions play an important part in the corporate culture. If there is no professional debate, then it must be created. In the discussions one must be able to communicate one's message clearly. One's message must be distinguishable from other messages, and this requires that one understands it clearly oneself. It must be remembered that different groups in the organization have different interests. How does this affect the formulation of the message?

Exercise 11.2

Identify incentives and impediments in the change work

Discuss the corporate culture in your organization on the basis of Figure 11.2. Which three factors are the most powerful incentives, and which three factors are the most decisive impediments concerning change in your organization?

Below are listed eight factors that are supposed to characterize multinational corporations with financial success and innovative ability.

1. A bias for action.
   The company analyses the situation before taking action, but does not stay indecisively in the analysis.

2. Close to the customer.
   The company is service-oriented, and gets its ideas for new products and services from its customers.

3. Autonomy and entrepreneurship.
   The company creates leaders and supports innovations.

4. Productivity through people.
   The individual employee is the basis of quality and increased productivity.

5. Hands-on, value driven.
   The basic philosophy is more important to the company's results than are techniques, economy, and organization. Management is visible.

6. 'Stick to the knitting.'
   The company stays close to well-known business.

7. Simple form, lean staff.
   The organizational structure is simple, and there are few people on the staff.

8. Simultaneously loose–tight properties.
   The company is characterized by autonomy, but the core values are centrally controlled.

Discuss for each factor whether they act as incentives or as impediments in the change work.

What other properties act as incentives in the change work?

What will yield success and reward?

- Short-term solutions to acute problems, or long-term solutions to fundamental problems?

What is the attitude towards changing working practices?

- The topic is irrelevant.
- Can be solved by issuing directives.
- Should be planned as a project in its own right.
- Changes should take place permanently.

What is included in the system developers' domain of action?

- Only creating products.
- Or creating products, as well as changing the users' organization and work.
- Only organizing the system developers' own work.
- Or organizing own work, as well as the conditions of this work.

Figure 11.2   Relevant questions when studying the corporate culture.

It is difficult to talk about changing working practices. It is far more easy to talk about a specific tool or a specific method. The first thing to do is thus to simplify the message. For instance, talk about better project management, or — even more concrete — talk about reviews, estimation, and project establishment. However, the perspective must be clear, otherwise it will be a question of once-only efforts, and not about a coherent strategy for changing working practices.

11.3 Qualifications: training and experience

The change activities interact with the system developers' qualifications. Their present qualifications, on the one hand, determine what type of innovations can be implemented. The objective of the change work, on the other hand, is precisely to contribute to the development of the participants' qualifications.

A prerequisite for employing a new method is that you must know something about it. But you do not master the method until you have worked with it for some time. This may sound trivial, but two of the most popular approaches to change work actually ignore this statement. Firstly, there is the strategy that is based on standards. The assumption here is that if you tell people how they should work, they will automatically follow your instructions. Secondly, there is the strategy of sending people on courses. The assumption here is that if you send them off to these courses, they will return with the qualifications required for changing working practices. Both strategies ignore the facts that it takes time to incorporate new working practices, and that there is a need for both experiments and follow-up activities.

Present qualifications

Exploit the differences in qualifications and experience

The present qualifications in a systems development organization — both the strong and the weak aspects of these qualifications — constitute an important starting point for the change work. Both experience and formal education must be considered. Professional conflicts are not uncommon in projects made up of a mix of some people with long practical experience and some less experienced people with a theoretical background. It is a main goal, when planning change work, to point out the necessity of, and make use of, both types of qualifications. The different groups have a lot to learn from each other.

You may get a picture of the qualification requirements if you employ the mapping techniques described in Chapter 6. If these techniques are used on current and concluded projects, this may indicate what type of qualifications ought to be developed. If the system developers themselves participate in mapping activities like this, they will become aware of deficiencies in their own qualifications, and this may prove an important motivation.

The mapping activity may indicate that many of the technical, product-oriented qualifications are good. This is the core of the professional traditions. However, there is an increasing need today for qualifications in project management, and in analysis, design, and realization of the interaction between computer technology and the users' other work. There is a lack of process- and organization-oriented qualifications. There is also a lack of knowledge of alternative working practices, and of the methods described in the literature on systems development. This obviously delimits the kind of suggestions the system developers themselves can come up with. General deficiences may be improved through initiatives on an organizational level. Sections 11.4 and 11.5 look at how these initiatives can be put in motion.

Exercise 11.3

Map the qualification requirement

Map one or several completed or current projects in your organization. Determine what events or phenomena have been significantly positive and negative. Discuss the reasons why these events and phenomena have occurred. Divide the reasons according to whether they have anything to do with the working practices in the project or with conditions outside the project. On this basis work out a list of activities that the system developers should be better at performing if the same problems are to be avoided in the future. Consider what kind of qualifications are necessary, and how they can be acquired.

The change work is also made more difficult if there is no shared conceptual framework concerning the products being developed and the work being performed. If these shared concepts are not present, it will become difficult to process and systematize experience. It will also become difficult to communicate within and across the projects. Hence the change work should contribute to establishing shared concepts.

Education and practice

There are, as already mentioned, two ways of acquiring qualifications: formal education and practice. A development organization may employ both types. By planning a project carefully you may obtain an effect that surpasses anything a training course could manage. It is obviously still a good idea to send the system developers on courses, but the best educational effect is obtained on courses for the whole project group, where the exercises and discussions are related to current needs.

Building up experience usually takes place in an unorganized way.

It is possible to strengthen the creation of experience by letting one or more system developers be apprentices working with an experienced and competent person. This person is not supposed to do or manage the work of the apprentice, but to guide the apprentice to figure out for himself how it should be done. If no one in a project masters a specific activity, a system of mutual guidance could be organized.

A consultant is ideal for increasing qualifications. A consultant may act both as a teacher and as a guide, and there is no risk that the consultant is swallowed up by development work.

This section has argued that it is the responsibility of management to develop the qualifications of the employees, especially in relation to performing process-oriented tasks. The remaining part of this chapter looks at some strategies used in the change work today (Section 11.4). Section 11.5 draws up a more efficient strategy.

11.4 Strategies for change

Why is it necessary to create more professional working practices in systems development? The primary goal of the development organization in this connection is to increase productivity. Increased productivity may result in the following improvements:

- Improved products and services.
- Decreased consumption of resources.
- Fewer unpleasant surprises in the projects.

The first two are difficult to measure. The same project is never performed twice, so the quality and the consumption of resources cannot be directly compared from one project to another. Hence it might be a good idea to go for the third goal of productivity. Chapters 5–7 presented a number of suggestions for how this can be done.

Another effect of more professional working practices is that the system developers feel more satisfied in their work because they handle it better. And this is probably the strongest motivation for changing working practices. Even though the system developers and the development organization may have many motives and objectives in common, it would be foolish to ignore the possible conflicts. Many

Rigorous adherence to directives. You do not promote a professional working practice merely by telling the system developers how they should do their work.

organizations find themselves in a situation where the amount of orders exceeds the capacity, where the project efforts are underestimated, and where poor product quality requires increasing maintenance. In situations like that the organization has some short-term goals which conflict with spending time on discussing professional working practices — even though this would be the only sensible thing to do.

Traditionally there are three different types of strategic options to increase productivity in systems development: distributing standards and manuals, training, and purchasing new tools. Each strategic option is an important ingredient in an overall strategy for changing working practices. However, on their own they will rarely lead to the goal, but rather give rise to inexpedient situations which will be discussed under the headings of 'rigorous adherence to directives', 'fixation on courses', and 'the mythical tool'.

Rigorous adherence to directives: the paralysed methods department

Rigorous adherence to directives is linked to the existence of a methods department which cooperates with the system development projects only through distributing guidelines and standards.

Since the mid-seventies it has become fashionable to establish a staff function with responsibility for methods issues in larger development organizations. A characteristic of such staff functions is that they see it as their main task to work out company-specific manuals and standards, which they then try to 'sell' to the system developers. At best this activity results in a new and good standard spread throughout the organization. However, standards more often end up collecting dust on a shelf because — as described in Chapter 2 — there is a greater need for situation-determined working practices than for standards.

At worst — if the standards are poor or are not disseminated properly in the organization — the standards will become millstones around the system developers' necks. The consequence of this would be a feeling of antagonism between the methods department and the rest of the development organization. The system developers might even end up refusing to discuss working practices at all because practice has shown them that this does not have any effect on their problems. The result could be that the methods department concentrates on describing its own methods proposals in professional magazines and presenting them at conferences.

Fixation on courses: knowledge without change

Another way to change working practices in systems development is to participate in some of the many courses organized by professional associations or private firms. These courses are often very effective when it comes to teaching a new programming language, a new diagramming tool, or the operation of a new operating system. However, many participants have felt that it can be difficult to convince others of the advantages of their new knowledge once they return home. If the courses are to have any effect — apart from disseminating general information — they must be selected so that they enter into an overall plan of carrying out a desired change. The plan should ensure that the issues taught at the courses can be tested in practice when the participants return home.

The mythical tool

The concepts tool and method are often confused so that the name of the tool is associated with the procedural solution to a problem. One reason for this is that the tool is a more tangible quantity (often a product) than a method. Tools have the advantage that they can be bought. Methods must be learned.

Tools are easily brought into focus. However, learning a new programming language does not necessarily lead to better programs. It is also necessary to discuss things like programming style and forms of cooperation. Systems descriptions on their own do not communicate better insight because a new description tool has been employed. It is also necessary to discuss what it is that should be communicated and between whom.

If the new tool is to be a help to better systems development, the starting point should be to determine the problems of employing the existing tools. Other important issues to discuss are what types of activities the tools support, and in which organizational and methodological environment they can be employed.

Resources

How many resources should a development organization spend on changing working practices? Our answer is 10 per cent of the man-hours spent on development and maintenance. It is difficult to give a theoretical argument for this figure. The pay-off of an investment like that is a corresponding improvement in products and services, a decrease in the consumption of resources, and improved project management. But all this is, as already mentioned, difficult to measure and prove.

Instead we will argue pragmatically that the development organization should start by setting aside 4 to 5 per cent of the man-hours entering into development and maintenance and spend it on change work. In the course of 5 to 6 years this figure could be increased to the 10 per cent we consider necessary if the innovative work is to have any permanent effect in the whole development organization. Most development organizations will need some time to implement this principle because most corporate cultures are characterized by inertia.

11.5 Innovation integrated in the project work

In this section we suggest a new way to organize change work in a systems development organization. Major parts of this suggestion have been tested with successful results in different types of companies, ranging from a company with an internal software department, through data service companies, to a company producing hardware as well as software. The companies had a staff of between 40 and 170 system developers. So far there is only limited experience with how the suggestion works as a whole.

The basic idea

The basic idea of the suggestion is that a group of system developers is formed which, concurrently with their practical work in the projects, spend 25 per cent of their time on initiating and organizing change work in the development organization.

In the following the group is called the methods group. Furthermore there are a number of case holders. A case holder is a person from a project who needs the support of the methods group to change working practices in a project. They are called case holders because the work of introducing new working practices within a limited subject area will be called a case.

The results should show up in the projects

The basic principle is that the work of changing working practices should be anchored in the projects. It is in the projects the results should be seen. And it is the projects that can obtain the results, because the projects already represent a concentration of qualifications and creativity, and because the projects, as social entities, are important to the formation of corporate attitudes.

The support from the methods group should be an offer to the projects — not an injunction. Responsibility for the projects, and the projects' relations to the development organization, are not affected. The methods group is not a control measure in relation to the work in the projects. Hence the group is not responsible for the success of the project it is supporting. However, the methods group is obviously professionally responsible for the quality of the advice it supplies, and for evaluating the quality and effect of the innovative work.

The suggestion represents a low-energy solution in as much as it can be implemented on a minor scale without investing millions on training and tools. The methods group should work dynamically and experimentally. The idea is to create new possibilities by experimenting with new working practices — not to create new limitations. The idea is to create learning processes — not to produce directives.

Organization

Replacement of members to ensure dynamics

Organizationally the methods group should refer to the development manager. Time consumption should thus be reported here. One of the participants in the methods group is appointed to be the organizational coordinator, but otherwise the group should be made up of people who can handle a collective form of management.

The group should consist of four to six members. Fewer people would make it difficult to help more than a few projects, and more people would result in internal coordination problems in the methods group. To ensure the dynamics without risking the continuity in the group's work, a systematical replacement of one or two of the people in the group twice a year is recommended. This replacement furthermore has the effect that an increasing number of people in the development organization obtain an active understanding of changing working practices.

The appointment of the members of the methods group is important. Members should be appointed according to their commitment and motivation. Other criteria are professional respect among colleagues and variety where education and experience are concerned. Members may be appointed by the development manager on the basis of applications from candidates and recommendations from the methods group.

The case holders are associated with the methods group as long as their case is running. The case holder is responsible for the case in question and should thus represent his or her project group in the methods group. The case holder is a kind of project leader on the case, and may, for instance, be responsible for making notes that disseminate the obtained results.

Management's role in relation to the methods group is first, through words and action, to indicate the importance of the methods group's work, and secondly to provoke the methods group to think in new ways.

The methods group should have the possibility of calling in external consultants, partly to guide the methods group itself, and partly to help the methods group with its activities.

Activities

The methods group has two types of activities, as can be seen from Figure 11.3: firstly, cases that consist of project support within limited subject areas; secondly, basic activities. The methods group arranges meetings every two or three weeks to discuss the course of the cases and plan other basic activities. The basic activities include professional lectures by employees in the development organization presenting their experience, or people from outside presenting new ideas. The basic activities may also include making notes documenting the experience

Cases (support within limited subject areas):

- Problem investigation.
- Project establishment.
- Project planning.
- Estimation.
- Reviews.
- System description techniques and system description tools.

Basic activities

- Meetings in the methods group.
- Professional lectures.
- Seminars.
- Documenting experience.

Figure 11.3 Methods group activities.

from the methods work. Finally the methods group should arrange a two-day seminar every six months at which the overall strategy is discussed.

Not all cases need initiate from the requirements of a specific project. The methods group can take the initiative to start experiments in one or more projects. If, for instance, description tools prove to be a general problem in the development organization, the methods group can choose two or three description tools and ask people in different project groups to test them. A case like this might not be successful in all the involved projects; but the development organization will gain very useful experience.

Figure 11.3 lists a number of subject areas for the cases. It is a good idea to start the change work in the individual project around a relatively delimited subject, for instance within project management activities. We return to that in Chapter 12.

Problems

Problems may arise in connection with the work of the methods group. The first one could be that the methods group does not get started, even though someone suggested it. In this case stronger arguments may be needed. Evidence like documented successes is convincing. That is why it pays to start on a small scale in your own project.

Another problem could be that there is no continuity in the methods group because of the replacements that were supposed to ensure innovation and dynamics. This problem can be solved by letting the biannual seminars act as handing-over seminars in which both the old and the new members of the group participate. The group should also be on the outlook for new possible candidates. When advising the projects, the methods group has the opportunity to identify candidates among the most interested project participants.

A third problem could be that motivation falls and the work comes to a stop. One way to solve this is through the regular replacement of members. Another way is to get inspiration from outside, for instance by bringing in external consultants who can act as motivators. Furthermore the methods group should constantly be on the outlook for situations where it can offer its services to the projects (for instance when a new project is established) instead of merely waiting for the initiative of the projects.

*Give high
priority to
interaction with
the projects*

Finally there is the risk that the methods group develops into, or is forced into, the role of a traditional staff function. The group must counteract this by giving high priority to direct and active interaction with the projects.

The suggestion for organizing the change work presented above is based on practical experience. Experience indicates that if new working practices are to be incorporated, it is important to establish an active cooperation between the projects and a project-independent unit that can act as support. Furthermore, experience indicates that active management support is necessary to keep motivation up and ensuring reasonable conditions for the innovative work. Even with a relatively small investment (5 per cent of the time spent on development and maintenance) it is possible to obtain more methodical working practices.

Further reading

The discussion of corporate culture in Section 11.2, and part of the suggestion for organizing the innovative work in Section 11.5 is based on Christensen and Molin (1984). The eight factors characterizing multinational companies in Exercise 11.2 are taken from Peters and Waterman (1982). Finally the chapter builds on practical experience with change work. This experience is documented in MARS 8 (1985), MARS 9 (1985), and MARS 10 (1985).

12 Learn in the project

Changing working practices requires an open mind and experiments

A system development project is the participants' best opportunity to learn new working practices. The project often provides the opportunity to participate in courses or to read scientific literature. Project work provides an inspiring background for trying out new ideas. The participants often represent different qualifications which provide the opportunity to learn from each other. This chapter presents experience from practical experiments of changing working practices as an integrated part of system development projects.

This chapter gives some directions as to how working practices can be changed systematically within the setting of a project. Section 12.1 discusses how the changes are initiated. Section 12.2 discusses the prerequisites of changing working practices: accumulation of experience and attainment of new knowledge. Section 12.3 looks at types of situations suitable for experimenting with working practices, and Section 12.4 discusses how you can handle the difficulties that may surface along the way. Section 12.5 questions the predominant view on systems development as a discipline.

12.1 Where do you begin?

It is difficult to change working practices in systems development. Firstly, this is because changing working practices is almost always given second priority compared to developing the computer-based system, which is usually seen as the one and only objective of the project. Secondly, changing working practices requires investment of resources. Thirdly, colleagues' attitude to changing working practices may not always be positive. Many excuses could be listed for not changing status quo. But if you belong to those who wish to improve their professional qualifications, the first problem is to get started. To deflate these excuses, you must be able to promise short-term benefits in the form of better systems, satisfied users, a more transparent project, or surplus resources. Later — by which time it is hoped that the attitudes to changing working practices have become more positive — more long-term criteria for changes can form the basis of the choice of object area. These may take the form of improved qualifications of the system developers, re-allocation of responsibility between the user organization and the development organization, or more systematic documentation.

Practical experience from trying to change working practices indicates that project management activities, for example, project establishment and reviews, are good starting points. It is easier to change project management practices than it is, for example, to introduce new description tools for analysis and design. The reason for this is that project management may be improved considerably even with a relatively modest input of resources.

It is recommended that you start with activities like project establishment, project planning, reviews, and estimation. Later you can move on to changing the product-oriented activities like maintenance or overall and detailed design. Once you start to discuss project management it will lead to discussions of working practices in analysis, design, or realization. If, for instance, you are carrying out project establishment activities, you will have to discuss the suitability of the employed description tools.

Plan the change

Before a change is initiated, it is important to draw up a plan. The plan should stipulate the necessary preparations, for instance in the form of training. The change should be an integrated part of the project work itself, and the plan should call for accumulation and dissemination of experience.

Give the
change a name
When planning the change activities it is important to formulate a basic philosophy. The change should have a name. The name could be the name of the technique employed (for instance 'review'), the activity (for instance 'systematic estimation'), or the product type (for instance 'overall design standard'). A name enables the participants to talk about the change and distinguish it from other (competing) activities.

The plan of the change activities should be incorporated in the project plan, and if individual system developers plan to develop their own professional qualifications, it is important to coordinate with these. The system developers' most important motivation for participating in the innovative activities is obviously that this work contributes to his or her professional development.

To illustrate the ideas behind changing working practices, two examples of how it can be done will be drawn up. They come from a company with a methods department which offers assistance to the projects in the form of consultants, as described in Chapter 11. If there is no methods department, there might be a quality assurance department, or there might be an experienced system developer whom the project group trusts, and who could act as consultant.

Example 1: Review of the project plan

The first example is about review of the project plan. A project is about to start. The product to be developed is a functional expansion of an existing administrative system. The project is expected to last 8 months with a staff of 3 to 5 people. In this situation the methods department offers to assist the project with a consultant.

The consultant discusses the situation with the project leader. The project is staffed with experienced people, and a number of standards from the existing system are available. No problems are anticipated where the product-oriented part of the system is concerned. On account of relations with the customer, the project must finish on time. The project leader worries that the plan may slip half-way through the project. The consultant points out the necessity of a good plan that will ensure that problems are seen in time, and suggests that the project group concentrates on working out a project plan. A meeting between the consultant, the project leader, and two project participants — who are going to be involved in the planning process — is arranged to take place three days later.

The meeting, which lasts for about an hour, starts off by discussing the situation in the project. The consultant finds that the project leader and the two project participants share the same view of the situation. The consultant presents a minimum standard for the project plan (see the suggestion in Chapter 5), and this standard is discussed. The consultant talks about the objective of reviews, about the various roles, and about the report.

The three project members expect to have the first version of the plan ready in two weeks, when a review is arranged. The consultant finds two reviewers among experienced system developers in other projects. The consultant makes sure that the reviewers receive the first version of the plan and points out which evaluation criteria they should follow: Does the plan facilitate project management? Does it meet the requirements in the minimum standard? Does the plan describe a realistic course of events?

The review itself follows the guidelines in Section 6.4. The consultant chairs the meeting, and one of the reviewers takes down the minutes of the meeting. The reviewers present their positive and negative general comments which are more or less identical: the plan as a whole is thorough, but a few sections lack detail and precision, and certain implicit assumptions are dubious.

Now the individual sections of the plan are discussed. The review leader makes sure that the producers answer only direct questions about the project.

The review is concluded, and everybody agrees that the plan only needs to be revised on a number of points. These points are described in a list of deficiencies. Further reviews are considered unnecessary. The project participants revise the plan during the following week, and this formally concludes the change activity.

Result:
- *Better plan*
- *More commitment*
- *Introduction to a new technique*

The short-term result of the review was that the participants were inspired to work out a better plan. Now they can feel more confident of the quality of the plan, and more people feel committed by the plan. The long-term effect is that the participants have been introduced to the review technique, and that they might apply it on their own initiative on later occasions. This constitutes the real change.

Example 2: Maintenance documentation

Another example is about improving the maintenance documentation. A group of seven system developers maintain a large administrative system developed two years earlier. Two of the system developers are relatively new in the organization. They work full-time on maintaining the system. The other five developers participated in developing the original system. They spent between 5 and 50 per cent of their time on maintaining the system.

The methods group arranges a meeting for the whole system development organization. At the meeting they talk about their work. Afterwards the audience split up into groups according to their projects. A consultant from the methods group participates in each group. The groups are to discuss how they can use the methods group.

It turns out that the above-mentioned maintenance group has a lot of problems. There is a long list of maintenance requirements which have not been met. The documentation is full of deficiencies. Parts of the system can only be maintained by specific people. No one has an overview of the situation. There is disagreement in the group. The new employees think that the solution would be to get the older system developers to document their own system. And the older employees think that the new system developers should make an effort to get to know the system.

The consultant suggests that the group should form a study circle on maintenance documentation. This study circle should work out a documentation standard for the system, and they should plan how the existing documentation could be improved. This suggestion is accepted by the group, and a few days later the consultant hands over a plan for the study circle. The plan is shown in Figure 12.1. The circle meets about once a month. The group approves the plan.

Result:
* *Comprehensive view of problems*
* *Solutions initiated*
* *Improved working practices*

The course of events more or less follows the plan. The maintenance group seems to have obtained a comprehensive view of the problems, and has started to solve them. Even though the cooperation in the group was not an item on the agenda, it has improved. Part of the reason for this is that the consultant insisted that the group discusses the maintenance documentation without personal confrontations (whose fault it was, who should pull themselves together, etc.).

These two examples, which are based on real events, illustrate that system development practices can be improved considerably with a relatively modest investment of resources.

1st meeting
* Discuss what good maintenance documentation is on the basis of the recommendations in literature.
* Make a list of the system's existing documentation.

2nd meeting
* Discuss how a part of the system documentation could be improved.
* Discuss typical maintenance tasks and the documentation they require.

3rd meeting
* Discuss a draft of a documentation standard.
* Discuss an example of revised documentation.
* Work out a plan for improving the overall documentation.

4th meeting
* Revise standard and plan.
* Discuss the course of the study circle.

Figure 12.1 Plan for study circle on maintenance documentation.

Exercise 12.1

Plan for developing qualifications

What would you like to work with in your next project (a) during the next 3 years; (b) during the next 10 years? Have you planned how to qualify for it? Do you think your management has a plan for developing your qualifications?

12.2 Learn from your own and others' experience

Discussing experience with other projects

Discussing experience with other projects is an important element in developing qualifications and attitudes in a systems development organization. The activity helps to minimize the feeling of insecurity

Poor working practices. An important element in developing qualifications and attitudes in a system development organization is to exchange experience across projects.

when introducing new working practices, and the discussions contribute to establishing the company's social environment.

One way of exchanging experience is that the project group enlists people from other projects as reviewers or advisers. Another way is that the project group presents its experience to people in other projects. To ensure that the project group really does effect its own intentions, it would be a good idea to plan and advertise these activities.

Accumulating experience

A prerequisite of exchanging experience with others is that the project group is aware of its own experience. After the project has been concluded, the project group should try to identify the problems and discuss if they could have handled them differently. This would help the system developers to anticipate the problems in their next project. It might even be possible to avoid the same problems in the future, or at least minimize their consequences. It is obviously also important to discuss and analyse the project's successes. Accumulation of experience should include a description of the course of events, the problems and successes — what caused them and what their consequences were — and a discussion of possible alternative working practices and how they could have been introduced. Figure 12.2 is an

---

A project conclusion report could have the following list of contents:

About the product:

1. Evaluation of the system — technically and in relation to the users.
2. Rejected and unmet requirements.
3. Post-calculation of the costs of the project.
4. List of documentation.
5. Suggestions for improving methods.

About the process:

1. Descriptions of the course of the project.
2. Problems, causes, and effects.
3. Successes, causes, and effects.
4. Alternative procedures.
5. Actions that should have been initiated to realize the alternatives.

Figure 12.2   List of contents of a project conclusion report focusing on both the product and the process.

example of a list of contents of a project conclusion report focusing on both the product-oriented part, as well as on the process-oriented part of the project.

Consultants, courses and literature

Convey knowledge and inspiration
Another way to develop qualifications is to hire consultants. The consultant brings new knowledge into the project and ensures that attention is paid to the change activities.

Courses in subjects concerning systems development can be a good source of inspiration if the subject and the timing are relevant in relation to the project work. It is a good idea to send several project participants on the same course so that they can discuss the ideas when they return home. A company sent a project group on a course to learn a specific system description technique. The project group had found that the technique in question would be suitable in their project. The technique turned out to be a success when employed in the project. On this background the company's management decided that all system developers should attend a similar course, and that the technique in question should be introduced as a standard. However, this proved not quite as successful. The technique was not applied in the analysis and design activities, but only afterwards in the documentation in order to satisfy the steering committees.

Reading literature is a fourth way of improving qualifications. Chapter 13 will present some ideas of how a project can organize the reading of this book, for instance in study circles.

Exercise 12.2

Make a plan for increasing your knowledge

Choose a subject area that your present project lacks knowledge about. Make a plan that ensures that the project obtains this knowledge.

12.3 Good opportunities

A project will find itself in situations where it seems obvious to discuss working practices and how they can be changed. It is important to be aware of these situations and not neglect the opportunity to improve working practices in the project. On the other hand, not all situations are suitable for discussing and changing working practices. If a project group, for instance, is trying to finish an intermediate product on time, it should forget all about changing working practices. The most important opportunities for changing working practices in a project are listed in Figure 12.3.

When is the right time to try out new ideas?
Working practices have already been discussed in connection with project establishment, planning, and evaluation in Chapters 4–7. This will not be considered here. Instead the last two situations from Figure 12.3 will be discussed. When a new working practice is to be tested, it is important to be aware of expedient opportunities. If new people are joining the project group, or if someone expresses a desire for changes, this represents good opportunities that should not be missed.

Opportunity: new people joining the project

New people joining established projects are often regarded with scepticism. Even if they represent a much-needed increase in resources, it is still bothersome to introduce the new person to the project's standards, existing intermediate products, and established working

---

- Project start, project establishment.

- Baseline is reached, detailed planning of future work.

- Crisis in the project, problematic situations.

- New people join the project.

- Desire for change.

Figure 12.3   Good opportunities for changing working practices in a project.

practices. Neither is it easy to be the new person. Some of the activities performed in the project might seem strange, unnatural, or impractical. Existing documentation might be impossible to read because it is incomplete, incomprehensible, or incoherent. How do you say this without hurting the professional pride of the old project participants? The situation might lead to unconstructive conflicts. Or the new participants may slowly fall into and join the project's way of working. In both cases the project has lost an opportunity to change working practices.

Instead the project group could decide on the next internal status meeting to let the new project participant review the project plan. After that the group should discuss where the new participant fits into the plan, which changes this would require, and how it could be done.

Opportunity: desire for change

The best opportunity is when some of the project participants express a desire for change. This implies a positive attitude to change, and this attitude should be respected by the other participants. But first the proposal should be discussed thoroughly. What type of qualifications are required to facilitate the change? Are there any people available who have any experience in using the technique? To what extent should the new technique be applied on the various activities? What are the advantages and disadvantages? What are the alternatives? Any opportunity to discuss new working practices represents a planning situation where experience and knowledge should be combined and result in new and realistic ideas.

12.4 Difficulties are challenges

Changing working practices in a project will usually meet difficulties. This does not necessarily mean that you are heading along the wrong track. Maybe the difficulties arise because the task is more difficult than the project group anticipated. What matters in a situation like this is to learn more and act according to what has been learned.

Figure 12.4 illustrates four typical problems that may arise in connection with changing working practices. This section will discuss some of the things that can be done to counteract the problems.

Patience and stubbornness

It would be naive to expect that changes happen on their own just because people have agreed upon making them. Successful changes are often characterized by the fact that at least one person has stubbornly kept on pushing for them. Preferably this person should be somebody from the project group, but a consultant might also play this role. If the change still comes to nothing, the situation should be mapped (see Section 6.5). The involved people's view on, and evaluation of, the situation should be brought out into the open. The reasons for failure to incorporate the change should be made clear. Is the reason lack of motivation and understanding of the benefits? Are the participants right in assuming that the change is without any benefits? If the change moves in a different direction, it is important to find out why this happened. Maybe this new direction is a good development. But how can the project group systematically support the new development? The change may be met with enthusiasm in the beginning, but after a while things come to a stop. Mutual commitment to success must be established in situations like that. Motivation is an on-going and a self-increasing process.

The project group may find that the change takes too long. Maybe the participants — especially the ones who took the initiative — were too optimistic in the beginning. It is important to be patient and create realistic expectations. These expectations should be based on the relation between investment and benefits and on the visibility of the results. The project group might, for instance, spend 20 hours on setting up reviews of intermediate products. These 20 hours might well be earned again in the form of improved product quality, improved coordination,

---

- Lack of commitment. Activities agreed upon are not carried out.

- The change moves in another direction. The contents of activities are changed.

- A good start, but it fades out.

- Things move too slowly.

Figure 12.4   Typical difficulties in changing working practices in projects.

and improved project management. These things cannot be measured, but maybe it turns out that the project runs into fewer problems than other projects. And this is not a bad thing either.

12.5 Research and practice

Systems development always has an element of experiment

This chapter will be concluded by a discussion of the relation between development of knowledge and professional practice. Working practices are changed constantly. When performing a given work process the participants keep on developing new knowledge about the work process: its nature, possible procedures, and possible tools to help perform the process. However, practitioners are not very conscious about this. At least, they do not talk very much about it.

One way of understanding our work better is to compare it to other professions. Most system developers compare themselves to engineers, but system development also includes elements that can be found in work performed by architects, town planners, therapists, and managers.

The traditional concept of systems development as a technical profession leads to one set of working practices, while identification with the other professions mentioned above leads to other sets of working practices. Below we have illustrated this by taking a closer look at the use of experiments, and the relationship between practice and research.

Different objectives of experiments

Many professions carry out experiments. In the traditional scientific concept an experiment is a test of a hypothesis. The result of the experiment is a rejection or a confirmation of the probability of the hypothesis. However, there are other perspectives on experiments. One perspective sees an experiment as an exploration. The goal is unclear beforehand, the objective is to learn more about the object of the experiment. The experiment might be to test a new programming tool to learn about its properties. Another perspective sees an experiment as action testing. The goal is to obtain a result and — if the action is successful — to study the effects of the action. The experiment might be to investigate the expediency of a proposed solution on a small scale before implementing it on a large scale.

The same experiment will often have elements of all three types of objectives: concurrently explorative, action testing, and hypothesis testing. One objective may be dominant, but it is useful to be aware of the other two.

Two competing views

The attitude to one's profession is of decisive importance to both the ability and willingness to change working practices. Table 12.1 compares the traditional view on systems development with an alternative and more embracing view.

In the traditional perspective the objective of a task is given beforehand. The question is to choose the best method. If there are no suitable methods to choose from, this is a research task that must be solved first. In systems development analysis, design and realization are temporally separated and are performed in this sequence.

In the alternative perspective working practices are developed dynamically through experiments with new techniques and tools. There is no difference on grounds of principle between practice and research, even though there obviously is a difference in the primary objective: practice results in products and services and research results in knowledge. In systems development analysis and design takes place in dynamic interaction, and realization reveals the need for new analysis and design activities.

	Traditional view on systems development	Alternative view on systems development
The relation between goals and means	The goal is given, e.g. in the form of a requirement specification. The question is to find the techniques and tools with which to realize the goals.	The techniques and tools are selected in an attempt to realize a goal. Goals change currently, among other things because new techniques and tools present possibilities of realizing new, and so far unobtainable goals.
The relation between research and systems development	Systems development makes use of theories and methods that were developed in previous research projects.	Systems development has elements of research. Methods and results within systems development and research overlap.
The relation between knowledge and action	In systems development, development of knowledge comes before action.	Development of knowledge and actions are inseparable in systems development.

Table 12.1   Two different views on systems development.

The alternative view is not the one and only view. However, in our opinion it is — as the previous chapters hopefully indicated — the most embracing one.

These considerations on experiments and on professional attitude are obviously also important where changing working practices is concerned. Regardless of whether the change (seen as an experiment) is successful or not, you have learned something, and you should make clear to yourself what it is you have learned. If you wish to learn more, and you wish the change to be successful, you must keep on experimenting. The change activities, as they have been discussed in this chapter, are an extension of the alternative view on systems development. When the changes are integrated in the project activities, they resemble research, in which it is necessary to have an experimental attitude to learn from the experience gained along the way and — if necessary — change working practice.

Further reading

The chapter is based on practical experience with changing working practices. This experience is documented in MARS 8 (1985), MARS 9 (1985), and MARS 10 (1985). The discussion in Section 12.5 of research and practice is based on Schön (1983), Kensing (1985) and Jepsen and Nielsen (1986). This and the following chapter are both inspired by Illeris (1984).

13 The book in practice

One thing is to read, another to use and understand

13.1 Apply the book in the projects
13.2 Arrange a department meeting
13.3 Arrange a study circle

This book does not contain the final truth about systems development. It has arisen from an ambition to write about some of the experience and possibilities that may form the background for action in the individual projects or development organizations. To make this vision a reality this book should not merely be read — it should be applied in practice.

The book may be applied in connection with project activities, and it may be applied in traditional discussion and training activities. System development projects are learning processes, and they contain many possibilities for further training and exchange of experience. Section 13.1 will present some ideas for how this book can be applied in a project. Section 13.2 will present some ideas for how the book can be applied in the professional discussions in the development organization. Section 13.3 will describe the book's applicability in education.

13.1 Apply the book in the projects

Make systematic use of the possibilities for training in the projects

A project almost always offers the participants an opportunity to improve their qualifications. There are challenges and possibilities enough to learn something new. However, in practice these training opportunities are rarely exploited systematically. The project plan must include training. This may be the best use of the resources from the training budget.

If the training opportunities in the project are to be fully exploited, the development organization must support these efforts. The training aspect should enter into the project activities on equal footing with other aspects, for instance in connection with setting the goals, selecting the participants, and determining the setting of the project. Examples of educational goals in the project work are illustrated in Figure 13.1.

Applying this book should be seen in this overall context. But where does the book enter into the work on a more concrete level? It is envisaged that the book will be applied to project work in the following ways:

• During project establishment.

Use the book. A crisis in the project is a good opportunity to seek new inspiration.

- As reference manual.
- In connection with crises and problematic situations.
- When planning experiments.

Use the book during project establishment

     The first, and perhaps best, opportunity to discuss working practices in the project is when the project is established. The book may be applied in two ways. Firstly, the book contains advice and guidelines for planning the establishment activities (Chapter 4). Secondly, the book may be used as an inspiration when planning the working practices in

---

- The project participants should, when the project is concluded, have worked with specific professional areas that are relevant to the project.

- The project participants should be thoroughly acquainted with the project's methods and have insight into cooperative relations and the solution of cooperative problems.

- The project participants should describe and evaluate the course of the project for the information or instruction of other employees.

- The project should qualify individuals to undertake project management functions in future projects.

Figure 13.1 Examples of goals for training in a development project.

the project. The book contains advice and guidelines for the most important activities in systems development (Chapters 5 to 10), and it contains a discussion of the possibilities and problems linked to changing working practices (Chapters 11 and 12). Discuss these chapters as part of the project establishment activities, and use the chapters as a basis for planning the project. Selected chapters could be presented at the establishment meetings, and the book could act as manual when the project charter is worked out.

Use the book as a reference manual in other situations

The practice-oriented chapters have been written with the intention of offering advice and support in relation to some of the typical activities in system development projects. Chapters 5 and 7 are a support during planning activities. Chapters 8 and 9 are a support in the analysis and design activities. In other words, use the book in your work.

Crises or problematic situations in the project are good opportunities to look critically at the working practices.

Exercise 13.1

Evaluate the training

- Give some examples of how your qualifications as system developer have been improved by participating in a development project.

- Evaluate your qualifications in the areas that are normally required and developed in a development project:

  (a) Application knowledge.
  (b) Ability to organize your work and solve your assignments.
  (c) Multidisciplinary and problem-oriented way of working.
  (d) Ability to cooperate with others.
  (e) Flexibility in relation to changing work tasks.
  (f) Ability to understand the people you work with and other people affected by the project.

- What further training have you received during the past two years? How has this influenced your working practices?

Generally the book contains some ideas for different or new working practices that may be employed when planning experiments in the project. The wish to experiment may be caused by a crisis or a problematic situation, but there are — as already mentioned in Chapter 12 — other situations that may lead to the desire to change working practices in the project. The innovations should first and foremost take place through experiments. Use the book to generate ideas, and as a basis for planning the experiments.

13.2 Arrange a department meeting

Initiate discussions of working practices

Changing working practices requires and leads to discussions among the employees in the development organization. This book may be used as a tool in these discussions.

If you want to promote the idea of experimenting with working practices, it may be a good idea to arrange a meeting for the whole department. Work out an introduction illustrating how the change activities are carried out today and how many resources are spent on this account. Supplement with the ideas and attitudes in Chapters 11 and 12. Start a discussion on the department's policy and practice in this field. Prepare a proposal for how the change activities could be arranged, and make the proposal an object for discussion.

A department meeting may also discuss current or concluded experiments in the department. A meeting like that may help disseminate experience across the projects, and the discussion will stimulate the professional debate in the department. Work out an introduction describing the experiment. Supplement this description with an evaluation of the course of the experiment: how does the experience from the experiment correspond with the theories and techniques in this book (especially Chapters 4 to 10), and how does the experience from changing working practices correspond with the ideas in Chapter 12? Start a discussion on this basis. Prepare a proposal for how this experience could be disseminated to other projects, and make the proposal an object for discussion.

13.3 Arrange a study circle

This book can also be used more traditionally in connection with private study, courses and study circles. As a counterpart to the more traditional courses within the field of computer technology, it would be a good idea to collect small groups of colleagues in a study group on this book. The study circle may be called 'Systems development in theory and practice' and run over 5 or 10 sessions, depending on how deeply you wish to explore the subject.

The basic idea is to compare the theories, ideas, and attitudes in the individual parts of the book with the experiences in the projects in which the people in the study group have participated. Before every session a subject or a chapter is selected, and the participants are expected to read the material beforehand. One of the participants introduces the session with a presentation of relevant experience, and the material is discussed on this basis. Study circles should be action-oriented, so that part of the result consists of a number of concrete suggestions for initiatives on department level, or ideas for experiments in the participants' own projects.

The end.

Bibliography

Andersen, P.B. (1985), *Semiotics and Informatics: Computers as media*, Department of Information and Media Science, Aarhus University.

Andersen, P.B. and A. Kjær (1984), *Description Tools for Development and Evaluation of Computer Technology in Organizations*, Department of Information and Media Science, Aarhus University (in Danish).

Bersoff, E. (1980), *Software Configuration Management*, Prentice Hall, Hemel Hempstead.

Blegen, H.M. and B. Nylehn (1974), *Organization Theory*, Tapir, Trondheim (in Norwegian).

Boehm, B.W. (1981), *Software Engineering Economies*, Prentice Hall, Hemel Hempstead.

Borum, F. and H. Enderud (1981), *Conflicts in Organizations: Illustrated by studies of systems development*, Nyt Nordisk Forlag (in Danish).

Budde, R. *et al.* (1984), *Approaches to Prototyping*, Springer Verlag, Berlin, Heidelberg.

Checkland, P. (1981), *Systems Thinking, Systems Practice*, J. Wiley, Chichester.

Christensen, S. and J. Molin (1984), *Project Organization as a Method for Innovation and Change*, Danish Project Society (Foreningen Projektplan) (in Danish).

Ciborra, C. (1981), 'Information systems and transaction architecture', *Journal of Policy Analysis and Information Systems*, **5** (4).

Dahl, B.O. (1982), *The Situation of the Project Manager: Functions, responsibilities and interests*, Master's thesis, Institute of Informatics, Oslo University (in Norwegian).

Davis, G.B. (1982), 'Strategies for information requirements determination', *IBM System Journal*, **21**.

Davis, G.B. and M.H. Olson (1984), *Management Information Systems: Conceptual foundations, structure and development*, McGraw-Hill, New York.

DeMarco, T. (1979), *Structured Analysis and System Specification*, Yourdon Press, New York.

DeMarco, T. (1982), *Controlling Software Projects*, Yourdon Press, New York.

Dunn, R. and R. Ullman (1982), *Quality Assurance for Computer Software*, McGraw-Hill.

Ehn, P. and M. Kyng (1984), 'A tool perspective on design of interactive computer support for skilled workers', in M. Sääksjärvi (ed.), *Report of the Seventh Scandinavian Research Seminar on Systemeering*.

Ehn, P. and Å. Sandberg (1979), 'Good analysis', in Å. Sandberg (ed.), *Analysis and Change within the Public Authorities*, Liber Forlag (in Swedish).

Elmaghraby, S.E. (1970), 'The theory of networks and management science', *Management Science Application*, **17**(2).

Enderud, H. (1976), *Decisions in Organizations*, Fremad, Copenhagen (in Danish).

Freedman, D.P. and G.M. Weinberg (1982), *Handbook of Walkthroughs, Inspections and Technical Reviews*, Little, Brown and Company, Boston.

Galbraith, J. (1973), *Designing Complex Organizations*, Addison-Wesley, Reading, Mass.

Gustavsen, B. (1977), *Organization: Alternative models*, Tanum, Oslo (in Norwegian).

Jackson, M. (1983), *System Development*, Prentice Hall, Hemel Hempstead.

Jepsen, L.O. and P.A. Nielsen (1986), *Diaries for Management of Systems Development*, Master's thesis, Computer Science Department, Aarhus University (in Danish).

Hansen, P.B. and P.J. Jensen (1985), *Estimation of Systems Development Projects: Practices, theory and experiments*, MARS-report no. 7, Computer Science Department, Aarhus University (in Danish).

Holbæk-Hanssen, E., P. Håndlykken and K. Nygaard (1985), *System Description and the DELTA Language*, Norsk Regnesentral, Oslo.

Illeris, K. (1984), *Making Project Work Useful: Through exploitation of the educational potential for project work and through experience of project work within educational institution*, Danish Project Society (Foreningen Projektplan) (in Danish).

Kammersgaard, J. (1985), *Four Different Perspectives on Human-Computer Interaction*, DAIMI PB-203, Computer Science Department, Aarhus University.

Kensing, F. (1985), 'Systems development: possibilities for and obstacles to changing practices', in *Proceedings of Conference on Development and Use of Computer Based Systems and Tools*, Computer Science Department, Aarhus University, Denmark.

Knudsen, J.L. and K.S. Thomsen (1985), *A Conceptual Framework for Programming Languages*, DAIMI PB-182, Computer Science Department, Aarhus University.

Kraft, P. (1977), *Programmers and Managers: the routinization of computer programming in the United States*, Springer Verlag, New York.

Lanzara, G.F. (1983), 'The design process: metaphors and games', in U. Briefs *et al.* (eds), *Systems Design for, with and by the Users*, North Holland, Amsterdam.

Lanzara, G.F. and L. Mathiassen (1985), 'Mapping situations within a system development project', *Information Management*, **8**(1).

Lucas, H.C. (1985), *The Analysis, Design and Implementation of Information Systems* (3rd edn), McGraw-Hill, New York.

MARS 2 (1984), *Systems Development in Praxis: Jutland Telephone*, MARS-report no. 2, Computer Science Department, Aarhus University (in Danish).

MARS 3 (1984), *Systems Development in Praxis: RC79*, Aarhus, MARS-report no. 3, Computer Science Department, Aarhus University (in Danish).

MARS 4 (1984), *Systems Development in Praxis: Computing Center of the Danish Savings Banks*, MARS-report no. 4, Computer Science Department, Aarhus University (in Danish).

MARS 5 (1984), *Systems Development in Praxis: EAC DATA*, MARS-report no. 5, Computer Science Department, Aarhus University (in Danish).

MARS 8 (1985), *Changing Working Habits in Systems Development: Jutland Telephone*, MARS-report no. 8, Computer Science Department, Aarhus University (in Danish).

MARS 9 (1985), *Changing Working Habits in Systems Development: RC 79*, MARS-report no. 9, Computer Science Department, Aarhus University (in Danish).

MARS 10 (1985), *Changing Working Habits in Systems Development: EAC DAT*, MARS-report no. 10, Computer Science Department, Aarhus University (in Danish).

Mathiassen, L. (1981), *Systems Development and Systems Development Methods*, PhD thesis, DAIMI PB-136, Computer Science Department, Aarhus University (in Danish).

Mathiassen, L., B. Rolskov and E. Vedel (1983), 'Regulating the use of Edp by law and agreements', in U. Briefs *et al.* (eds.), *Systems Design for, with and by the Users*, North Holland, Amsterdam.

Martin, J. and C. McClure (1985), *Structured Techniques for Computing*, Prentice Hall, Hemel Hemstead.

Mikkelsen, H. and J.O. Riis (1981), *Fundamentals in Project Management*, Promet, Copenhagen (in Danish).

Mikkelsen, H., J.O. Riis and H.J. Schmidt (1984), *Managing Administrative Systems Development Projects*, Promet, Copenhagen (in Danish).

Mumford, E. (1985), 'Defining system requirements to meet business needs: a case study example', *The Computer Journal*, **28**(2).

Munk-Madsen, A. (1978), *System Description with Users*, DUE note no. 9, Computer Science Department, Aarhus University (in Danish).

Munk-Madsen, A. (1984), 'Practical problems of system development projects', in M. Sääksjärvi (ed.), *Report of the Seventh Scandinavian Research Seminar on Systemeering*.

Munk-Madsen, A. (1985), 'Evaluation of System Development Projects', in *Proceedings of Conference on Development and Use of Computer Based Systems and Tools*, Computer Science Department, Aarhus University.

Naur, P. (1984), *Programming as Theory Building*, Microprocessing and Microprogramming 15, North-Holland, Amsterdam.

Naur, P. (1985), 'Intuition in software development', *Proceedings of the International Joint Conference on Theory and Practice of Software Development*, Springer Verlag, Berlin.

Nygaard, K and P. Håndlykken (1980), *The System Development Process — its Setting, some Problems and Needs for Methods*, Norwegian Computing Centre, Oslo.

Nygaard, K. and P. Sørgaard (1985), 'The perspective concept in informatics', in G. Bjerknes *et al* (eds), *Computers and Democracy*, Avebury.

Ouchi, W.G. (1980), 'Markets, bureaucracies and clans', *Administrative Science Quarterly*, **25**.

Parnas, D.L. and P.C. Clements (1985), 'A rational design process: how and why to fake it', in *Proceedings of the International Joint Conference on Theory and Practice of Software Development*, Springer Verlag, Berlin.

Peters, T.J. and R.H. Waterman, Jr. (1984), *In Search of Excellence*, Harper & Row, New York.

Schön, D.A. (1983), *The Reflective Practitioner*, Basic Books, New York.

Schönfeldt, B. (1983), *Development of Cooperation in Projects: How to start projects*, Danish Project Society (Foreningen Projektplan) (in Danish).

Yourdon, E. (1982), *Managing the System Life Cycle*, Yourdon Press, New York.

Index